Old Friends

Treasured Tales From Childhood

2004
TO Claudyne & Bruce —
Old Friends, dear friends &
above all Cape May friends!
Best Wishes!
Elliot Engel

Dr. Elliot Engel
Quinn Hawkesworth

Copyright and Publishing Information

ISBN: 1-890123-62-5

This book was originally published in 1996, but was thoroughly revised and expanded (with many new illustrations) in November 2002
First Authors Ink Printing November 2002
Second Authors Ink Printing October 2003

For information regarding special discounts for bulk purchases, please contact Authors Ink at 800-392-4434 or sales@authorsink.com

Book design by Carl Gilfillan
Printed by Media Consultants, Inc.
Raleigh, NC

Cover illustration and other original artwork by Quinn Hawkesworth
Typesetting by Denise Clark

Printed in the U.S.A.

Old Friends
Table of Contents

Table of Contents (continued)

Introduction

Old Friend:
"That special individual whose presence alone doubles our joys and halves our sorrows."
Oliver Wendell Holmes

This book is actually a thorough revision and expansion of the **Old Friends** volume we published in 1996. The immediate success of that book convinced us that not only are old, old friends cherished but that even a new **Old Friends** might be welcomed.

In any case, our name for the book was inspired by Oliver Wendell Holmes' definition of an Old Friend: "That special individual whose presence alone doubles our joys and halves our sorrows." We have filled this volume with children's literature which we believe accomplishes that same rare feat. We call these pieces "old friends" because we all meet them as children and then, far too often, fail to revisit most of them as we grow older. Our hope is that this book might acquaint youngsters with some of the most memorable stories and poems ever written and reacquaint adults with the readings that enthralled them so many years ago.

Most of these stories are passionate in tone and theme because children's emotions are so fervent. For example, as children we experience an especially instinctive unity with the natural world. E.C. Spykman in the wonderful *A Lemon and a Star* brilliantly recreates that childhood time when nature was a living entity in this description of a young boy playing at a brook: "He squatted on his haunches, passing the pebbles over and through his fingers. Not only was the discovery of the mud his, but this brook was his. He did not see it as a made stream, but as the ancient buried water which in the old days used to run through fields and swamps and which refused to get lost when the flood came down on top of it. He loved it, he loved this obstinate heroic brook, and his hands went back and forth making a pet of the water."

We've divided our treasure chest of literature into the most common individual compartments: enchantments, adventure, people and animal stories, myth, tales both humorous and horrific, and cradlesongs. Quinn Hawkesworth has been invaluable both in selecting so many of her personal childhood favorites and in providing many of her exquisite drawings. Quinn and I give special thanks to Denise Clark for guiding the contents every step of the way with her subtle suggestions and keen questions and to Carl Gilfillan for assembling all the materials with flawless taste and with wondrous illustrations which complement Quinn's. I have supplied a short essay which opens each of the literary sections. Most of these appeared first in my column ("In Plain Engel-ish") in *Authors Ink*, our newsletter. The essays do not relate directly to the specific works; instead, they are reflections on broader literary and personal memories.

May you turn and return to these stories and poems far more than once upon a time, and may the delight contained within them enable you to strive for that illusory yet illustrious goal of living happily ever after. Enjoy!

Elliot Engel
Raleigh, North Carolina
November 15, 2002

Introduction

Enchantments

I can think of no more beloved Old Friend than my love of reading. This essay reveals the very personal inspiration for my favorite hobby.

Charles Dickens

Essay

by Dr. Engel

When I give a talk to a large audience on Dickens, I can always count on at least two questions being asked. Since my lecture credits Dickens with inventing both the mass-market paperback book and the soap opera, there is always someone who will politely but dubiously ask: "Can everything you said *really* be true?"

I'm always delighted with this question, because it shows the innate optimism of my audience. Here is someone who seriously doubts that I've stayed within even the broadest bounds of truth during the lecture; yet by asking this question, he implies that I shall now mend my lying ways and answer with the truth, the whole truth, and nothing but the truth.

My answer never varies: "I swear that 90% of the information I gave you on Dickens is absolute gospel." And the other 10%, I add, is hardly a lie but rather my interpretation. The glory of literature, as opposed to math, is that, like our family and friends, there is always a mystery in it.

The other question I'm always asked is: "Where did you get your great love of Dickens?" The short answer would be: from a professor at UCLA where I did my PhD work. I was smart enough to find out during my first week as a graduate student which professor was the best in the entire department. Her field just happened to be Dickens. I'm sure that if her field had been Colonial American Literature, I would now be leading a "Cotton Mather Club." As this wise professor once told me, "There is no author so great that a terrible teacher cannot ruin, nor is there any author so terrible that a great teacher cannot make brilliant."

But to me the most interesting question, which nobody ever asks, is: "Why do you love reading?" It is the love and respect for the written word which is ultimately more important than any particular author. And I am certain when my initial glee from reading began.

I was about eight years old. Every summer my father promised me one trip to Riverside Amusement Park in Indianapolis, where I grew up. It was the highlight of my entire year. As soon as we entered the park that summer, I spotted a young man selling helium balloons. I begged for one, and Dad agreed. I selected an emerald green balloon, for it was then and has remained my favorite color. Dad warned me to hold very tightly to the string or else the balloon would float away.

With the peculiar logic of an eight-year-old, I decided I'd let go of it for just a second so that I could enjoy the thrill of catching the string right before it was too late. Robert Browning said that man's reach should exceed his grasp—but not so with little boys. That balloon quickly exceeded not only my reach and my grasp but my father's as well.

Up and up it flew, leaving behind one heartbroken little boy crying far below. Dad did not lecture me, nor did he buy me a replacement. Quite soon, the excitement of the rides made me feel better. But I did not forget about that balloon.

At breakfast the next morning, I asked sadly, "Where do you think my balloon is now?" "Well, Elliot," I can still hear my father say, "since the wind was blowing toward the East, your balloon must now be over Ohio." Where's Ohio? Dad walked over to a bookshelf

Up and up it flew, leaving behind one heart-broken little boy crying far below.

"It is a wise father who can turn a minor disaster at an amusement park into the inspiration for an amusement that will last my entire life."

in our den, pulled down the "O" volume of the *World Book Encyclopaedia*, and showed me the colored map of Ohio. I'll never forget the pale green of the state with all the speckley large and small black dots which located the various Ohio cities. The memory, in fact, revives every time I eat mint-chocolate-chip ice cream.

Dad then read to me all about Ohio, my balloon's temporary home. I was intrigued. The next morning, of course, I asked about the location again and was told the balloon was over Pennsylvania. But where's Pennsylvania? This time Dad took down the proper volume, but it was *I* who started—slowly—to read about my balloon's latest home. By the time that balloon was over New Jersey, I had fallen in love with maps, geography, the encyclopedia, and—most especially— words. It is a wise father who can turn a minor disaster at an amusement park into the inspiration for an amusement that will last my entire life.

Queen Mab

by William Shakespeare

She is the fairies' midwife

She is the fairies' midwife, and she comes
In shape no bigger than an agate-stone
On the fore-finger of an alderman,
Drawn with a team of little atomies
Over men's noses as they lie asleep;
Her wagon-spokes made of long spinners' legs.
The cover of the wings of grasshoppers,
Her traces of the smallest spider web,
Her collars of the moonshine's watery beams,
Her whip of cricket's bone, the lash of film,
Her waggoner a small grey-coated gnat,
Not half so big as a round little worm
Prick'd from the lazy finger of a maid;
Her chariot is an empty hazel-nut
Made by the joiner squirrel, or old grub,
Time out o' mind the fairies' coachmakers.
And in this state she gallops night by night
Through lovers' brains, and then they dream of love;
On courtiers' knees, that dream on curtsies straight;
O'er lawyers' fingers, who straight dream on fees;
O'er ladies' lips, who straight on kisses dream,
Which oft the angry Mab with blisters plagues,
Because their breath with sweetmeats tainted are.
Sometimes she gallops o'er a courtier's nose,
And then dreams he of smelling out a suit;
And sometime comes she with a tithe-pig's tail
Tickling a parson's nose as 'a lies asleep,
Then dreams he of another benefice.
Sometimes she driveth o'er a soldier's neck,

And then dreams he of cutting foreign throats,
Of breaches, ambuscadoes, Spanish blades,
Of healths five fathom deep: and then anon
Drums in his ear, at which he starts and wakes,
And being thus frightened, swears a prayer or two,
And sleeps again. This is that very Mab
That plats the manes of horses in the night;
And bakes the elf-locks in foul sluttish hairs,
Which once untangled, much misfortune bodes.

William Shakespeare

*Shakespeare, an English playwright and poet, was born on April 23, 1564 and died on the **same date** in 1616. During his writing career of 21 years he wrote 38 plays—**Romeo and Juliet** is probably his most popular. Shakespeare became a wealthy man not by writing plays, but by the profits generated by his acting company when his plays were performed. Shakespeare is the most quoted author in history, so if you have ever said "**break a leg,**" or been "**in a pickle,**" or "**refused to budge an inch,**" or "**slept not one wink,**" or "**laughed yourself into stitches**," then you have quoted Shakespeare.*

The Frog Prince

by the Brothers Grimm

...but the face of the youngest was radiant as the sun.

In olden days there lived a King whose daughters were all beautiful, but the face of the youngest was radiant as the sun.

The favorite plaything of this Princess was a golden ball. Often when it was too hot to play in the palace gardens, she would wander with her ball into the forest, and toss or bounce it under the shade of an old lime tree. Then, when she grew tired, she would sit by the edge of a cool well beneath the lime, and wish it might be summer all the year round.

One bright morning the Princess was playing as merrily as ever with her golden ball. Toss, catch, toss, catch, toss—but this time the Princess did not catch. The ball fell on the sloping grass, rolled straight into the silver well, and immediately disappeared.

The poor Princess sat down and wept as if her heart would break. Nothing, she felt, could ever make up for the loss of her golden ball.

As she cried bitterly, sitting by the edge of the well, she was startled to hear a voice ask, "What is the matter, Princess?"

Looking round, she saw a frog stretch its broad, ugly face out of the water.

"Oh, it is you, is it, old Splasher?"

"Yes; what is the matter, Princess?"

"Matter? I want my ball, my golden ball. It has fallen into the water."

"There is no need to cry about that; I can bring it to you."

"Oh, thank you, thank you, dear Frog."

"But what will you give me, when I bring you your golden ball?"

"Oh, anything, anything—my silken robes, my pearls, my diamonds, even my crown."

"What care I for silken robes, for pearls, for diamonds, or even the crown you wear upon your head? If you will promise to let me sit at your table, eat off your golden plate, drink from your silver cup, and sleep in your little white bed, then I will fetch you the golden ball."

"Yes, yes, I promise. Bring it. Quick."

The Frog disappeared under the water, and the Princess thought, "What nonsense the silly old Splasher talks. Of course, he cannot come with me to the palace. This well in the forest is his home, and here he must live and croak until he dies."

In a little while the Frog came back, carrying in his mouth the golden ball. He threw it on the grass, at the feet of the Princess.

"Oh, my ball, my pretty toy," she exclaimed, as she picked it up, and ran off toward the palace.

"Wait, wait," croaked the Frog, "I cannot run so quickly."

But the Princess did not listen. She hurried home, rejoicing to possess once more her favorite plaything, but forgetful of the kind Frog and her promise.

The next day, as the Princess was sitting at dinner with the King and his courtiers, they heard a sound, as of something coming flip-flop upstairs. All laid down their knives and forks to listen. Flip-flop, flip-flop.

the Brothers Grimm

Jacob (1785-1863) and Wilhelm (1786-1859) Grimm were born in Germany and became famous for their classical collections of folk songs and folktales. The brothers wrote most of the tales from oral narrations collected from peasants and villagers. They wanted to capture the genuine oral tradition of the tales, unlike some of the "Mother Goose" stories that had been written 100 years before. Working together, Wilhelm selected and arranged the stories and Jacob was responsible for the research and scholarly work.

Enchantments

Then it ceased just outside the door of the dining-hall, and one knock after another was heard, while a voice croaked:

"Youngest King's Daughter,
Open to me,
Do you not know
What you promised me,
Yesterday
Under the linden tree?
Youngest King's Daughter,
Open to me."

"My daughter," said the King, "what you have promised, you must perform. Open the door."

So the Princess opened it, and the Frog came in and flopped along close to her feet, until she sat down.

Then he reminded her, "You promised I should sit at your table."

The Princess hesitated, but the King said, "What you have promised, you must perform."

So a chair was placed for the Frog by the Princess.

But the Frog asked to be put on the table. "You promised that I should eat off your golden plate and drink from your silver cup."

The Princess drew her plate away, and lifted the cup in her hand, but the King repeated, "What you have promised, you must perform."

So the Frog thoroughly enjoyed dinner, but the Princess could not swallow a morsel.

When evening came, the Frog said, "I am tired. Carry me now to your little white bed. We must sleep."

Then the Princess began to cry. How could she let that cold, slippery frog, that she could not bear to touch, sleep in her little bed?

But the King said once more, "What you have

So the Princess opened it, and the Frog came in and flopped along close to her feet, until she sat down.

promised, you must perform." Then he added, "You must never despise anything that has helped you in time of need."

So the Princess caught the Frog with the tips of her two fingers, and carried him upstairs to her own pretty room. There she put him down in a corner. But when she popped into bed, the Frog came jumping toward her and croaked, "You promised I should sleep in your little white bed. If you do not let me, I shall call the King."

"You hideous thing, you may sleep there," she exclaimed angrily, picking him up and flinging him with all her might against the wall.

The Frog struck the wall and fell to the ground. Then—the Princess rubbed her eyes. Who was that handsome Prince standing where the Frog had fallen? And where was the Frog? Was it a dream? The Princess pinched herself. No, she was wide-awake.

"I was changed into a frog," said the Prince, "by a wicked fairy, and a frog I remain until I was flung from the hand of a fair Princess. So you have saved my life, and I want, above everything in the world, to marry you, and to take you back with me to the kingdom that I left so long ago."

Then the face of the Princess was once more as radiant as the sun, and the King, when he heard the tale, was almost as glad as his daughter, and ordered the wedding feast to be got ready without delay.

And the day after the wedding, a golden coach, drawn by eight snow-white horses, dashed up to the palace gates, to carry the Prince back to his kingdom, and with him his fair bride.

Behind the coach rode Henry, the faithful servant whose heart had nearly burst with grief when his master was turned into a frog. Suddenly there came a loud

Who was that handsome Prince standing where the Frog had fallen?

Enchantments

. . . the Princess . . . rejoiced to think of all the good fortune it had brought to her and her dear Prince.

sound of cracking. Henry begged them to have no alarm. He was only tearing off the iron bands with which he had bound his heart to keep it from breaking.

As they rode gaily off, bowing to the cheering crowd, the horses pranced, the bells on the reins jingled, and all was rejoicing and merriment. As they passed the well in the forest the Princess drew from her pocket the golden ball, and rejoiced to think of all the good fortune it had brought to her and her dear Prince.

Pretty children they all were; but the prettiest was the youngest daughter. . .

East O' The Sun And West O' The Moon

A Norwegian Folk Tale

Once upon a time there was a poor husbandman who had so many children that he hadn't much of either food or clothing to give them. Pretty children they all were; but the prettiest was the youngest daughter, who was so lovely there was no end to her loveliness.

So one day—'twas on a Thursday evening late in the fall of the year—the weather was wild and rough outside. It was cruelly dark, and rain fell and wind blew, till the walls of the cottage shook again and again. There they all sat round the fire busy with this thing and that. Just then, all at once something gave three taps on the windowpane. The father went out to see what was the matter; and when he got out of doors, what should he see but a great big White Bear.

"Good evening to you," said the White Bear, politely.

"The same to you," said the man.

"Will you give me your youngest daughter? If you will, I'll make you as rich as you are now poor," said the Bear.

Well, the man would not be at all sorry to be so rich; but still he thought he must have a bit of talk with his daughter first; so in he went and told him how there was a great White Bear waiting outside, who had given his word to make them rich if he could only have the youngest daughter.

The lassie said "No!" outright. Nothing could get her to say anything else; so the man went out and settled it with the White Bear, that he should come again the next Thursday evening and get an answer. Meantime the man talked to his daughter and kept telling her of all the riches they would get; and how well off she would be herself. At last she thought better of it, and washed and mended her rags, made herself as smart as she could, and was ready to start. I can't say packing gave her much trouble.

Next Thursday evening came the White Bear to fetch her; and she got upon his back with her bundle, and off they went. When they had gone a bit of the way, the White Bear said,

"Are you afraid?"

"No," she said.

"Well! mind and hold tight by my shaggy coat, and there's nothing to fear," said the Bear.

So she rode a long, long way, till they came to a great steep hill. There on the face of it, the White Bear gave a knock; and a door opened, and they came into a castle, where there were many rooms lit up; rooms gleaming with silver and gold; and there was a table ready laid, and it was all as grand as it could be. The White Bear gave her a silver bell; and when she wanted anything, she had only to ring it, and she would get what she wanted at once.

Well, after she had eaten and drunk, and evening wore on, she got sleepy after her journey and thought that she would like to go to bed; so she rang the bell; and she had scarce taken hold of it before she came into a chamber where there were two beds made, as fair and white as any one could wish to sleep in, with silken pillows and curtains and gold fringe. All that was in the

Norwegian Folk Tales

The Norwegian cultural heritage holds many treasures. Popular story telling may be among the finest of these treasures. Folktales are free-ranging and imaginative stories which have passed from storyteller to storyteller from time immemorial. Like all good literature, they are based on real life, yet are never confined to reality or what is considered to be true and reasonable. Folktales begin and end calmly, and poetic justice is seen to be done: the good are rewarded and the evil are punished. There is always a happy ending.

Enchantments

So one Sunday, the White Bear came and said now they could set off to see her father and mother.

room was gold or silver; but when she had gone to bed, and put out the light, a man came in and lay down on the other bed. That was the White Bear, who threw off his beast shape at night; but she never saw him, for he always came after she put the light out, and before the day dawned he was up and gone again. So things went on happily for a while; but at last she began to grow silent and sorrowful; for she went about all day alone and she longed to go home and see her father and mother, and brothers and sisters, and that was why she was so sad and sorrowful, because she couldn't get to them.

"Well, well!" said the Bear, "perhaps there's a cure for all this; but you must promise me one thing, not to talk alone with your mother, but only when the rest are by to hear; for she will take you by the hand and try to lead you into a room alone to talk; but you must mind and not do that, else you'll bring bad luck to both of us."

So one Sunday, the White Bear came and said now they could set off to see her father and mother. Well, off they started, she sitting on his back; and they went far and long. At last they came to a grand house, and there her brothers and sisters were running about out of doors at play, and everything was so pretty, 'twas a joy to see.

"This is where your father and mother live now," said the White Bear; "but don't forget what I told you, else you'll make us both unlucky."

No, bless you, she'd not forget, and when she had reached the house, the White Bear turned right about and left her.

Then she went in to see her father and mother, and there was such joy, there was no end of it. None of them thought that they could thank her enough for all she had done for them. Now, they had everything they wished, as good as good could be, and they all wanted to know how she got on where she lived.

Well, she said, it was very good to live where she did; she had all she wished. What she said beside I don't know; but I don't think any of them had the right end of the stick, or that they got much out of her. In the afternoon, after they had finished their dinner, all happened as the White Bear had said. Her mother wanted to talk with her alone in her bedroom; but she minded what the White Bear had said, and wouldn't go upstairs.

"Oh, what we have to talk about will keep," she said, and put her mother off. But somehow or other, her mother got around her at last, and she had to tell the whole story. So she said, how every night, when she had gone to bed, a man came and lay down on the other bed in her room as soon as she had put out the light, and how she never saw him, because he was always up and away before the morning dawned; and how she went woeful and sorrowful, for she thought she should so like to see him, and how all day she walked about there alone, and how dull, and dreary, and lonesome it was.

"My!" said her mother; "it may well be a Troll sleeping in your room!" But now I'll teach you a lesson how to set eyes on him. I'll give you a bit of candle, which you can carry in your bosom. Just light that while he is asleep; but take care not to drop the tallow on him."

Yes, she took the candle, and hid it in her bosom, and as night drew on the White Bear came to fetch her away.

But when they had gone a bit of the way, the Bear asked her if all hadn't happened as he had said.

Well, she couldn't say it hadn't.

"Now mind," said he, "if you have listened to your mother's advice, you have brought bad luck on us both, and then all that has passed between us will be as

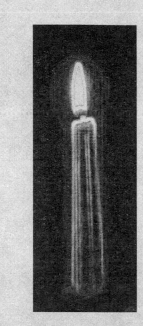

"I'll give you a bit of candle, which you can carry in your bosom. Just light that while he is asleep; but take care not to drop the tallow on him."

"Tell me the way, then," she said, "and I'll search you out; that surely I may get leave to do."

nothing."

"No," she said, "I haven't listened to my mother's advice."

When she reached home, and had gone to bed, it was the old story over again. There came a man and lay down on the other bed; but at dead of night, when she heard him sleeping, she got up and struck a light, lit the candle, and let the light shine on him, and she saw that he was the loveliest Prince she had ever set her eyes on and she fell so deep in love with him on the spot that she thought that she couldn't live if she didn't give him a kiss then and there. And so she did; but as she kissed him, she dropped three drops of tallow on his shirt and he woke up.

"What have you done?" he cried. "Now you have made us both unlucky, for had you held out only for this one year, I had been freed. For I have a stepmother who has bewitched me, so that I am a White Bear by day, and a Man by night. But now all ties are snapt between us; now I must set off from you to her. She lives in a castle which stands East o' the Sun and West o' the Moon, and there, too, is a Princess with a nose three ells long, and she's the wife I must now have."

She wept and took it ill, but there was no help for it; go he must. Then she asked him if she mightn't go with him.

No, she mightn't.

"Tell me the way, then," she said, "and I'll search you out; that surely I may get leave to do."

"Yes, you may do that," he said; "but there is no way to that place. It lies East o' the Sun and West o' the Moon, and thither you'll never find your way."

The next morning when she awoke, both Prince and castle were gone, and there she lay on a little green patch in the midst of the gloomy thick wood, and by her side lay the same bundle of rags she had brought with her from her old home.

When she had rubbed the sleep out of her eyes, and wept till she was tired, she set out on her way, and walked many, many days, till she came to a lofty crag. Under it sat an old hag, and played with a gold apple which she tossed about. Her the lassie asked if she knew the way to the Prince, who lived with his stepmother in the castle that lay East o' the Sun and West o' the Moon, and who was to marry the Princess with a nose three ells long.

"How did you come to know about him?" asked the old hag. "But maybe you are the lassie who ought to have had him?"

Yes, she was.

"So, so; it's you, is it?" said the old hag. "Well, all I know about him is that he lives in the old castle that lies East o' the Sun and West o' the Moon, and thither you'll come late or never; but still you may have the loan of my horse and on him you may ride to the next neighbor. Maybe she'll be able to tell you; and when you get there, just give the horse a switch under the left ear, and beg him to be off home; and, stay, this golden apple may you take with you."

So she got upon the horse and rode a long, long time till she came to another crag, under which sat another old hag, with a gold carding-comb. Here the lassie asked if she knew the way to the castle that lay East o' the Sun and West o' the Moon, and she answered, like the first old hag, that she knew nothing about it except it was East o' the Sun and West o' the Moon. "And thither you'll come, late or never; but you shall have the loan of my horse to my next neighbor; maybe she'll tell you all about it; and when you get there, just switch the horse under the left ear and beg him to be off home."

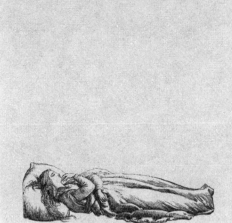

The next morning when she awoke, both Prince and castle were gone, and there she lay on a little green patch in the midst of the gloomy thick wood, and by her side lay the same bundle of rags she had brought with her from her old home.

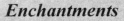

Enchantments

But if you will, I'll go to my brother, the West Wind; maybe he knows, for he is much stronger. So, if you'll just get on my back, I'll carry you thither."

And this old hag gave her the golden carding-comb; it might be she'd find some use for it, she said. So the lassie got up on the horse, and rode a far, far way, and a weary time; and so at last she came to another great crag, under which sat another hag, spinning with a golden spinning-wheel. Here, too, the lassie asked if she knew the way to the Prince, and where the castle was that lay East o' the Sun and West o' the Moon. So it was the same thing over again.

"Maybe it's you who ought to have had the Prince?" said the old hag.

Yes, it was.

But she, too, didn't know the way a bit better than the others. East o' the Sun and West o' the Moon it was, she knew—that was all.

"And thither you'll come, late or never; but I'll lend you my horse, and then I think you'd best ride to the East Wind and ask him; maybe he knows those parts, and can blow you thither. But when you get to him, you need only to give the horse a switch under the left ear, and he'll trot home himself."

And so, too, she gave the girl the gold spinning-wheel. "Maybe you'll find use for it," said the old hag.

Then on she rode many, many days, a weary time, before she got to the East Wind's house; but at last she did reach it, and then she asked the East Wind if he could tell her the way to the Prince who dwelt East o' the Sun and West o' the Moon. Yes, the East Wind often heard tell of the Prince and the castle, but he couldn't tell the way, for he had never blown so far.

"But if you will, I'll go to my brother, the West Wind; maybe he knows, for he is much stronger. So, if you'll just get on my back, I'll carry you thither."

Yes, she got on his back, and they went briskly along. When they got there they went into the West Wind's house; and the East Wind said the lassie he had brought was the one who ought to have had the Prince who lived in the castle East o' the Sun and West o' the Moon; and so she had set out to seek him, and now he had come with her, and would be glad to know if the West Wind knew how to get to the castle.

"Nay," said the West Wind, "so far I've never blown; but if you will, I'll go with you to our brother the South Wind, for he's much stronger than either of us, and he had flapped his wings far and wide. Maybe he'll tell you. You can get on my back, and I'll carry you to him."

Yes, she got on his back, and so they traveled to the South Wind and were not so very long on the way.

When they got there, the West Wind asked him if he could tell the lassie the way to the castle that lay East o' the Sun and West o' the Moon, for it was she who ought to have had the Prince who lived there.

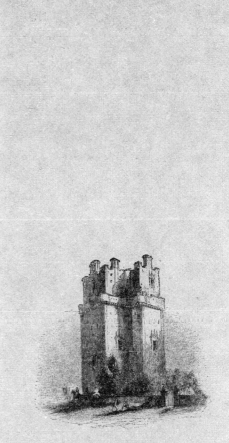

...the castle that lay East o' the Sun and West o' the Moon...

"You don't say so! That's she, is it?" said the South Wind. "Well, I have blustered about in most places in my time, but so far have I never blown; but if you will, I'll take you to my brother the North Wind; he is the strongest of the whole lot of us and if he doesn't know where it is, you'll never find any one in the world to tell you. You can get on my back and I'll carry you thither."

Yes, she got on his back and away he went from his house at a fine rate. And this time, too, she wasn't long on the way.

When they got to the North Wind's house, he was so wild and cross, cold puffs came from him a long way off.

"BLAST YOU BOTH, WHAT DO YOU WANT?" he roared out to them ever so far off, so that it struck them with an icy shiver.

"Well," said the South Wind, "you needn't be so foulmouthed, for here I am, your brother the South Wind, and here is the lassie who ought to have had the

Enchantments

Down below there was such a storm; it threw down long tracts of wood and many houses, and when it swept over the great sea ships foundered by the hundreds.

Prince who dwells in the castle that lies East o' the Sun and West o' the Moon; and now she wants to ask you if you ever were there, and can tell her the way, for she would be so glad to find him again."

"Yes, I know well enough where it is," said the North Wind; "once in my life I blew an aspen-leaf thither, but I was so tired I couldn't blow a puff for ever so many days after. But if you really wish to go thither, and aren't afraid to come along with me, I'll take you on my back and see if I can blow you thither."

Yes, with all her heart; she must and would get thither if it were possible in any way; and as for fear, however madly he went, she wouldn't be at all afraid.

"Very well, then," said the North Wind, "but you must sleep here tonight, for we must have the whole day before us if we're to get thither at all."

Early the next morning the North Wind woke her, and puffed himself up, and blew himself out, and made himself so stout and big 'twas gruesome to look at him; and so off they went high through the air as if they would never stop till they got to the world's end.

Down below there was such a storm; it threw down long tracts of wood and many houses, and when it swept over the great sea ships foundered by the hundreds.

They tore on and on—no one can believe how far they went—and all the while they still went over the sea, and the North Wind got more and more weary, and so out of breath he could scarcely bring out a puff; and his wings drooped and drooped, till at last he sank so low that the crests of the waves dashed over his heels.

"Are you afraid?" said the North Wind.

No, she wasn't.

But they weren't very far from land; and the North Wind had still enough strength left in him that he managed to throw her up on the shore under the windows of the castle which lay East o' the Sun and West o' the Moon; but then he was so weak and worn out he had to stay there and rest many days before he could get home again.

Next morning the lassie sat under the castle window and began to play with the golden apple; and the first person she saw was the Long-nose who was to have the Prince.

"What do you want for your gold apple, you lassie?" said the Long-nose, and threw up the window.

"It's not for sale for gold or money," said the lassie.

"If it's not for sale for gold or money, what is it that you will sell it for? You may name your own price," said the Princess.

"Well! If I may get to the Prince who lives here and be with him tonight, you shall have it," said the lassie.

Yes, she might; that could be arranged. So the Princess got the gold apple; but when the lassie came up to the Prince's bedroom at night he was fast asleep; she called him and shook him, and between whiles she wept sore; but for all she could do she couldn't wake him up. Next morning as soon as day broke, came the Princess with the long nose, and drove her out again.

So in the daytime she sat down under the castle windows and began to card with her golden carding-comb, and the same thing happened again. The Princess asked what she wanted for it; and she said it wasn't for sale for gold or money, but if she might get leave to go to the Prince and be with him for the night, the Princess should have it. But when she went up, she found him asleep again, and she called, and she shook him, and wept, and prayed, and she couldn't get life into him; and as soon as the first gray peep of day came, then came the Princess with the long nose, and chased her out again.

So in the daytime, the lassie sat down outside under

"What do you want for your gold apple, you lassie?"

Enchantments

the castle window, and began to spin with her golden spinning-wheel, and that, too, the Princess with the long nose wanted to have. So she raised the window and asked what the lassie wanted for it. The lassie said, as she had said before, it wasn't for sale for gold or money; but if she might go up to the Prince who was there, and be there alone that night, the Princess might have it.

Yes, she might do that and welcome. But now you must know there were some Christian folk who had been carried off thither, and as they sat in their room, which was next to the Prince, they had heard how the girl had been in there, and wept and prayed, and called to him two nights running, and they told that to the Prince.

That evening when the Princess came with her sleeping potion, the Prince made as if he drank, but threw the drink over his shoulder, for he could guess what kind of a drink it was. So when the lassie came in she found the Prince wide awake; and then she told him the whole story of how she came thither.

"Ah," said the Prince, "you've come just in the nick of time, for tomorrow is to be my wedding-day; and now I won't have the Long-nose, for you are the only lassie in the world who can set me free. I'll say I want to see what my wife is fit for and beg her to wash the shirt which has the three spots of tallow on it; she'll say yes, for she doesn't know 'tis you who put them there; but that's work for Christian folk, and not for a pack of Trolls; and so I'll say that I won't have any other bride than the lassie who is able to do that. If she can't she's not worth having."

Next day, she with the long nose began to wash away as hard as ever she could, but the more she rubbed and scrubbed, the bigger the spots grew.

"Ah," said the old hag, her mother, "you can't wash; let me try."

...the Prince made as if he drank, but threw the drink over his shoulder for he could guess what kind of a drink it was.

But she hadn't long taken the shirt in hand before it got far worse than ever, and with all her rubbing, and wringing, and scrubbing, the spots grew bigger and blacker, and the darker and uglier the shirt.

Then all the Trolls began to wash; but the longer it lasted, the blacker and uglier the shirt grew, till at last it was as black all over as if it had been up the chimney.

"Ah," said the Prince, "you're none of you worth a straw; you can't wash. Why there, outside, sits a beggar lassie. I'll be bound she knows how to wash better than the whole lot of you. Come in, Lassie!" he shouted.

Well, in she came.

"Can you wash this shirt clean, Lassie?" he said.

"I don't know," she said, "but I think I can."

And almost before she had taken it and dipped it in the water, it was as white as the driven snow, and whiter still.

"Yes, you are the lassie for me," said the Prince.

At that the old hag flew into such a rage, she burst on the spot, and the Princess with the long nose did the same and the whole pack of Trolls after her—at least I've never heard a word about them since.

As for the Prince and the Princess, they set free all the poor Christian folk who had been carried off and shut up there and they took with them all the silver and gold, and flitted away as far as they could from the castle that lay East o' the Sun and West o' the Moon.

"Yes, you are the lassie for me," said the Prince.

Enchantments

Adventure

Essay

by Dr. Engel

As a somewhat sedentary professor, I find my most exciting Adventures when exercising my wits in research. And it was my Old Friends—the numerous typewriters I owned as a boy—that first inspired these thrilling hunts.

I'm one of the few children who did not beg for a new model bicycle each birthday but instead always pleaded for an upgrade of my current typewriter.

Adventure

When I was a child I never spent one minute with my father in his workshop. There was no workshop. A complete inventory of the tools in the Engel household: one screwdriver, one hammer, and one wrench—all kept in the depths of the kitchen catch-all drawer. But I do vividly remember many times when I was dazzled by my father's manual dexterity. His instrument was neither a lathe nor a drill; it was a typewriter.

My father was an accomplished hunter-and-pecker who combined impressive speed, rhythm and accuracy. And so at a tender age of seven, watching him, I fell in love with everything connected with typing. I'm one of the few children who did not beg for a new model bicycle each birthday but instead always pleaded for an upgrade of my current typewriter.

I was enthralled the first time Dad boosted me up into his typing chair. I was so little that he needed to place the Indianapolis phone book beneath me (had we lived in a less populated city, I never could have reached the keyboard.) When I first put my tiny fingers on the middle-row eight keys, I assumed they would be resting on A-B-C-D-E-F-G-H, the same alphabetical order I had recently memorized and proudly recited hourly until my sister threatened to shut me up.

I tapped the "A" and it appeared, like magic, shining blackly against the white sheet of paper. But when I tapped what I thought would be "B", an "S" appeared. When I looked down at the keys, there were A-S-D-F-G-H-J-K-L, where A through H should have been.

I immediately asked my father what was probably my fiftieth question of that early Sunday morning: "Daddy, why did they put the letters in that order?" This time, for a change, it was a question worth asking. I still remember my father looking at the keys, thinking with furled brow, pausing, and then confessing: "Elliot, I don't know." There was another pause and then—"But I'll find out."

Of all the good examples my father bequeathed to me, the one I've probably appreciated the most as a teacher was his inability to give a facile guess to a question he could not answer. He always made it his mission to answer with accuracy, and I owe him an enormous debt for inspiring a love of research in me. He called the reference librarian at our downtown branch who told him she would have to do some checking and call him back. Imagine my glee in posing a question that not only stumped my brilliant father but even puzzled the "Reference Librarian," an august title which, to a seven-year-old, sounded like Merriam Webster himself.

She did call right back. Although I didn't fully understand his explanation to me at the time, Dad told me that the original typewriter designer worried about key jamming that would occur if the letter that had just struck the paper did not have time to fall back before the next arrived. And so the designer intentionally placed the letters on the keyboard in a difficult, illogical pattern to frustrate and slow the typist down to the capabilities of the machine. This slowing ironically made the process of typing more efficient.

I feel that there's a lesson here about the Virtue of Slow as we now speed into the computer age of Instant Information and Gratification, while the typewriter is joining the record player and slide rule on the shelves of future antique stores.

And so the designer intentionally placed the letters on the keyboard in a difficult, illogical pattern to frustrate and slow the typist down to the capabilities of the machine.

The act of reading a book is so much slower than watching a film or television show. Yet the demands made on us by following a narrative word by word often make the ultimate experience profoundly more rewarding. Similarly, with all the good answers my father patiently gave me during my childhood, it is his pauses that most impress me now, as he carefully thought about his responses, indicating not only a respect for the question but, even better, a respect for the questioner, his young son who adored him.

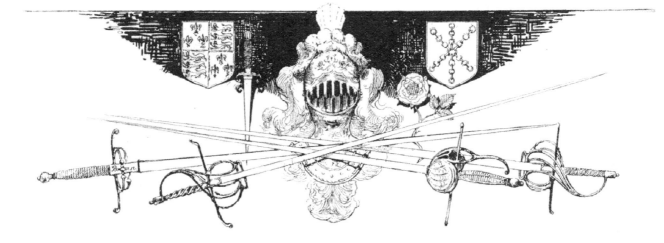

Travel

by Robert Louis Stevenson

I should like to rise and go
Where the golden apples grow;—
Where below another sky
Parrot islands anchored lie,
And, watched by cockatoos and goats,
Lonely Crusoes building boats;—
Where in sunshine reaching out
Eastern cities, miles about,
Are with mosque and minaret
Amongst sandy gardens set,
And the rich goods from near and far
Hang for sale in the bazaar;—
Where the Great Wall round China goes,
And on one side the desert blows,
And with bell and voice and drum,
Cities on the other hum;—
Where are forests, hot as fire,
Wide as England, tall as a spire,
Full of apes and cocoa-nuts
And the native hunters' huts;—
Where the knotty crocodile
Lies and blinks in the Nile,
And the red flamingo flies
Hunting fish before his eyes;—
Where in jungles, near and far,
Man-devouring tigers are,
Lying close and giving ear
Lest the hunt be drawing near,
Or a comer-by be seen

Adventure

Swinging in a palanquin;—
Where among the desert sands
Some desert city stands,
All its children, sweep and prince,
Grown to manhood ages since,
Not a foot in street or house,
Not a stir of child or mouse,
And when kindly falls the night,
In all the town no spark of light.
There I'll come when I'm a man
With a camel caravan;
Light a fire in the gloom
Of some dusty dining-room;
See the pictures on the walls,
Heroes, fights, and festivals;
And in a corner find the toys
Of the old Egyptian boys.

Robert Louis Stevenson

*Robert Louis Stevenson was born in Scotland in 1850. An only child, Robert was sick most of the time and could not attend school. He educated himself by reading all of the books in his father's library. He was a rebellious teenager and was known for his long hair and unusual clothes. His most famous work, **Dr. Jekyll and Mr. Hyde**, is neither a novel, a poem, a short story, nor an essay—it is known in English as a **novella**.*

Sindbad the Sailor

from The Arabian Nights

As Sindbad the Sailor was sitting in the mansion which he had built in the city of Baghdad, he heard a poor porter say: "Men are not rewarded according to their merit. I have worked harder than Sindbad, and yet he lives in splendor and I live in misery."

Sindbad was moved by the porter's complaint and invited him to come in and listen to the story of his adventures.

"Perhaps when you have learned by what sufferings I won my wealth," said Sindbad, "you will be more contented with your own lot in life."

"Look at my white hair and worn face! I seem an old man. But how young and strong I was when I sailed away to make my fortune by trading in strange countries! Soon after we departed, our ship was becalmed near a small island, but when we landed to look at the place, we found that what we had taken for land was only the green back of a great beast, a sort of ocean cow, called a whale."

"No sooner had we landed than it began to sway to and fro, and then it plunged beneath the waves and left us struggling in the sea. Clinging to a large piece of wood, I was washed ashore on a desert island."

"Here I thought I should have starved. But on wandering about I found a clump of fruit trees and hidden among them a great white ball about fifty feet in size. By this time I was very weary, and so when I had eaten some of the fruit I crept beneath the ball and lay down to sleep. Just as I was closing my eyes I looked up

"I found a clump of fruit trees and hidden among them a great white ball about fifty feet in size."

Adventure

and saw that the sky was darkened by the wings of a gigantic bird."

"'Good heavens!' I exclaimed. 'This great white ball is the egg of the monstrous bird that sailors call a roc.'

"And so it was. The roc settled on the egg under which I was lying, and one of its claws, which was as big as the trunk of a tree, caught my clothes."

"At daybreak the roc flew up into the air and carried me to such a height that I could not see the earth. Then it descended with such speed that I nearly lost my senses. As it alighted I freed my clothing and found myself in a deep valley cut off from the world by a circle of high, steep mountains."

"It was the Valley of Diamonds! The ground was covered with precious stones. Full of joy, I began to fill my pockets with them, but my joy was soon turned to terror. The valley was haunted by great serpents, and I could find no means of escape."

"I crept into a cave and blocked up the opening with a large stone, but all night I was kept awake by the hissing of the serpents. At daybreak they retired, as they were afraid of the roc that used then to visit the valley in search of food. Then I stole out of the cave, only to be knocked over by something that came tumbling down the mountain side. It was a great piece of fresh meat. As it rolled along, the diamonds on the ground stuck to it. Looking up, I saw on the mountains a band of men, who were about to roll another piece of meat into the valley."

" 'I have heard of this means of getting diamonds,' I said to myself. 'It strikes me that it is also a good means of getting away.'

"So I tied myself to the piece of meat and hid beneath it, and presently an eagle swooped down and seized the meat and carried it to its nest on the top of the

The Arabian Nights

The Arabian Nights is a collection of timeless Persian, Arabian, and Indian folktales handed down through several centuries. The original Arab title was "A Thousand Nights and a Night" or "1001 Nights." It is the story of King Shahryar who believes that all women are unfaithful and decides to murder his wives after their wedding night. This continues for three years, until the king marries the beautiful and resourceful Scheherazade. She decides to tell a tale to the king during their wedding night, and when the sun rises, she stops narrating, leaving the story unfinished. Shahryar is fascinated by the tale and does not kill Scheherazade, waiting for another night of story-telling. And thus she entrances him for 1001 Nights!

Adventure

"...but the roc followed us, bearing in its claws a great piece of granite."

"By the shore I met some sailors, with whom I returned to Baghdad."

Adventure

mountains. The band of men drove the eagle away, and turned the meat over to pick off the diamonds that had stuck to it, and found me tied to it.

"When we had all the diamonds we needed, we sailed for home. But on passing the desert island my companions landed with an ax and broke open the great white egg. A terrible scream rang through the sky. The roc had seen them. They rushed back to the ship, and we quickly sailed away; but the roc followed us, bearing in its claws a great piece of granite. This it dropped on our ship, and down we all went into the sea. Holding on to a fragment of wreckage with one hand, and swimming with the other, as the sea was calm, I managed to reach another island."

"It was a delicious spot! Sparkling streams ran between vineyards full of grapes and orchards full of fruit. There I met a strange old man, who made signs to me to carry him over one of the streams. As soon as I hoisted him on my back, the old man threw his legs over my neck and squeezed my throat so that I fainted. When I came to, he was still fixed on my shoulders. And there he remained."

"He made me his slave. When, in order to keep up my strength, I made some wine out of the grapes, he took it from me and drank it all up. Happily, it was too strong for him, and releasing his hold of my neck, he fell to the ground, and I killed him."

"By the shore I met some sailors, with whom I returned to Baghdad."

"'That was the Old Man of the Sea', they said to me. 'You are the first person that has escaped from being at last strangled by him.'"

"Now don't you think," said Sindbad to the porter, "that I have earned all the riches that I brought away from the Valley of Diamonds?" The porter agreed.

David and Goliath

From I Samuel 17:1-54
as adapted by May Hill Arbuthnot

"Choose a man from among you and let him come down to meet."

When Saul was king over Israel, the Philistines called together their armies for war against the Israelites. The Philistines were gathered at Shochoh, and King Saul and the men of Israel were gathered by the valley of Elah and they drew up in battle line facing the Philistines. And the Philistines stood on a mountain on the other side and there was a valley between them.

Then there came out a champion from the camp of the Philistines named Goliath of Gath. He was six cubits and a span high. He had a helmet of brass on his head, and he was armed with a coat of mail that weighted five thousand shekels of brass. He had greaves of brass upon his legs and a javelin of brass between his shoulders. The staff of his spear was as big as a weaver's beam and the spear's head weighed six hundred shekels of iron. A shield bearer walked before the champion.

Goliath shouted across the valley to the armies of Israel and said to them, "Why have you come out in battle array? Am not I a Philistine and you are the servants of Saul? Choose a man from among you and let him come down to meet. If he can fight me and kill me then we will be your servants, but if I overcome him and kill him, then shall you be our servants and serve us." And Goliath shouted again, "I defy the armies of Israel this day. Send me a man from among you that we may fight together."

When Saul and the Israelites heard the words of the champion, they were greatly frightened and knew not what to do. And Goliath the Philistine drew near, morning and evening for forty days, and shouted his challenge to the Israelites.

Now in Bethlehem, there was an old man named Jesse, who had eight sons, and the youngest was called David. The three oldest sons were Eliab, Abinadab, and Shammah, and they had followed King Saul to battle. David went with them, but later he returned to Bethlehem to care for his father's sheep. One day, Jesse said to David, "Take a measure of parched corn and these ten loaves and run quickly to the camp where your brothers are. And carry these ten cheeses to the captain of their thousand and find out how your brothers fare."

So David rose up early in the morning and left the sheep with a keeper and set off for the camp of the Israelites as his father had commanded him to do. He came to the camp just as the Israelites were making ready to go into battle. For the Israelites and the Philistines were both drawn up in battle line, army against army. For no man had accepted the challenge of Goliath the champion.

David left his supplies with a man who looked after such things and ran quickly into the battle lines looking for his brothers. Just as he found them and was talking to them, Goliath of Gath, champion of the Philistines, came out of the ranks and shouted his same words again, and David heard them: "Give me a man from among you that we may fight together."

Again, the men of Israel fled from the champion and were so afraid. They said to David, "Did you see this man who has come out to defy Israel? Surely the man who is able to kill this Philistine, King Saul will

**About I Samuel
in the Old Testament**

I Samuel is the ninth book in the Old Testament and was written in the 11th Century B.C. It is believed to have been written by Samuel, Gad, and Nathan, with Samuel writing the first 24 chapters. The book spans 100 years and includes what is believed to be the true historical accounts of Eli, Samuel, Saul, and David.

reward with great riches and give him his daughter in marriage and make his father's house free in Israel."

Then David said to the men standing by him, "What did you say shall be done for the man who overcomes yonder Philistine and takes away the shame of Israel? For who is this Philistine that he should dare to defy the armies of the living God?"

And the people told him again what King Saul would surely do for the man who could kill the Philistine.

But when Eliab, the oldest brother, heard what David said, he was angry with his younger brother and said to him, "Why have you come here and with whom did you leave those few sheep in the desert? I know your arrogance and the wickedness in your heart. You have come here because you want to watch this battle."

And David said, "What have I done now? And what cause have you to speak to me like that?" And he turned away from his brothers, and talked again with the men who answered him as before. And some of the words David spoke the men repeated to King Saul, and the king sent for David.

When David came before the king, the boy said, "Let no man's heart be afraid because of that Philistine. Your servant will go and fight with him."

But Saul looked at David and replied, "How can you expect to go against this Philistine to fight with him? You are only a boy, and Goliath has been a man of war from his youth."

Then David told the king this story. "Sometimes, when your servant was a shepherd with his father's sheep, a lion or a bear would come and take a lamb out of the flock. Then I would go after him and attack him and take the lamb out of his mouth. And when the beast rose against me, I would catch him by the beard,

"For who is this Philistine that he should dare to defy the armies of the living God?"

smite him, and kill him. Your servant killed both the lion and the bear, and this Philistine shall fare the same, for he has defied the armies of the living God. Moreover, the Lord who delivered me out of the paw of the lion and out of the paw of the bear, He will deliver me out of the hand of this Philistine."

So Saul said to David, "Go and may the Lord be with you."

Then, the king put his own armor on David. He put a helmet of brass on his head and armed him with a coat of mail. He also girded him with a sword over his armor. And David struggled to go, for he wanted to try the armor. But he said to Saul, "I cannot wear these, for I have not proved them."

And he took off the king's armor. Then David took his staff in his hand and he chose five smooth stones out of the brook and put them in a shepherd's bag which he had with him and, with his sling in his hand, he went out to meet the Philistine.

The Philistine came near to David, keeping his shield bearer directly in front of him. But when he came near enough to see David, he scorned him, for he saw that he was only a youth, ruddy and fair of face. And Goliath called out, "Am I a dog that you come against me with sticks?" And he cursed David and said, "Come on, and I'll give your flesh to the birds of the air and the beasts of the field."

David replied to the Philistine, "You come to me with a sword, a spear, and a shield, but I come to you in the name of the Lord of Hosts, the God of the armies of Israel, whom you have defied. This very day the Lord will deliver you into my hands, and I will smite you and take your head from your body and this day I will give your dead body and the dead of the camp of the Philistines to the birds of the air and the wild beasts

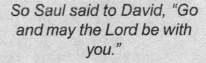

So Saul said to David, "Go and may the Lord be with you."

Adventure

David ran and stood over the Philistine and took the champion's own sword out of its sheath and slew him and cut off his head.

of the earth. This will I do that all the earth may know there is a God in Israel. And all this assembly shall know that the Lord saves not with sword and spear. For the battle is the Lord's, and He will give you into our hands."

And when David had finished speaking, Goliath drew near to meet him, and David ran towards the Philistine. And as he ran, he put his hand in his bag and chose a smooth stone. This he put in his sling and took aim. The stone struck the Philistine in his forehead, and he fell upon his face on the ground.

So David prevailed over the Philistine with a sling and with a stone and smote the Philistine and killed him. But there was no sword in David's hand.

Therefore, David ran and stood over the Philistine and took the champion's own sword out of its sheath and slew him and cut off his head. When the Philistines saw that Goliath, their champion, was dead, they fled. Then, the men of Israel arose and shouted and pursued the Philistines and plundered their tents.

David took the head of Goliath to Jerusalem, but he put Goliath's armor in the Philistine's tent.

Who Are You?

People In Poems

Essay

by Dr. Engel

As both a professor and national lecturer, I have been blessed by speaking to and meeting thousands of people. But I've learned that my general audiences are very different people from my students. However, the one thing they share is that so many of them have now become Old Friends.

"I just have one question: have you ever considered working for a circus?"

Who Are You?

I've always enjoyed public speaking more than "public" or even private writing, because the response to a speech is so much more immediate than to an essay or even a letter. There is nothing more gratifying to a public speaker than the loud applause followed by that excited buzz of grateful voices from an inspired audience after an especially good talk.

But it is the personal comments of those who come forward to speak to me following a lecture that impress me most. Almost all of the comments are quite supportive, though a few compliments are of the left-handed variety. I recall speaking in Atlanta on "Victorian Moral Guilt," a topic I felt deserved an enthusiastic yet quite dignified tone. After I'd finished, I remember silently congratulating myself on delivering a high-spirited yet rather sophisticated presentation. Moments later, a bouncy little woman hurried up to the podium and blurted out: "I just have one question: have you ever considered working for a circus?"

There are two comments, however, that I have heard at least ten times more than others. Please believe me when I tell you that I am repeating them here not because they are flattering (though they certainly are), but because they leave me uneasy. I have lost count of the number of times someone has come up to me after a talk and said either "If only I had had you for an English professor I would have made straight A's" or, even more often, "I would just love to enroll in one of your classes." Since I usually hear this last remark from audiences in Arizona, New Jersey or

Florida, I often deflect the praise by saying "Well, I appreciate that, but I'm afraid that the commute to class would wear you out."

I really am flattered that people hear my lectures and believe that I would be a favorite teacher of theirs. But I'm uneasy with their response for good reason. What they have just heard me deliver is a carefully prepared forty-minute talk on a favorite topic of mine, delivered to an adult audience usually as eager to hear it as I am to deliver it. This utopian situation should not be confused with the actual environment of the classroom. In high schools and colleges, instructors often find themselves having to prepare lectures on authors they either do not really like or, occasionally, do not fully understand. Also, during a busy semester these teachers may have less than two days for the research and preparation for a particular writer. And it should not be forgotten that they are going to be addressing a teenaged audience of students whose one most profound interest in the lecture material is usually: "Will any of this stuff be on the final exam?"

Because my audiences will not be tested on anything I say, they can (in the phrase of every airline pilot who ever addressed his passengers) "sit back, relax, and enjoy the flight" of my own imagination and rhetoric. Students in class, on the other hand, must take as many notes as possible and then pray that the eventual test will fairly reflect the lecture.

And so the ego rewards are greater when I lecture to adults, but the challenge is greater when I teach students. I sometimes view the differences between lecturing and teaching as starkly as that between thunder and lightning. As a lecturer, I can usually provide my audiences with some resonant thunderings and even professional pyrotechnics, full of sound and

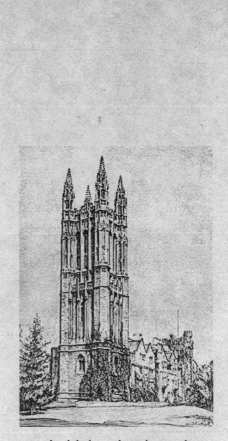

In high schools and colleges, instructors often find themselves having to prepare lectures on authors they either do not really like or, occasionally, do not fully understand.

Who Are You?

Thunder is good; thunder is impressive. But it's lightning that does the work.

hurry (I usually have less than 45 minutes), signifying—I hope—a great deal. But when I teach my own students, on good days I can bask in the lightning glow of seeing them become, under my direction, more sensitive to great literature, or, even better, more sensitive to their own essential selves. As any teacher knows, *that* experience is charged with a very special electricity. As to whether lecturing or teaching is more important to society, I do recall a favorite quotation from Mark Twain: "Thunder is good; thunder is impressive. But it's lightning that does the work."

Mark Twain

Emily Dickinson

Emily Dickinson was born (1830), lived, and died (1886) in Amherst, MA—never leaving the city. As a matter of fact, after the age of 25, she never left her house. She wrote 1775 poems during her lifetime, but they were not discovered until after her death. Her sister found them in a locked sewing box at the bottom of her closet. Because of family disputes over the poems, it took another 70 years for them to be published. It is interesting to note that Emily Dickinson never titled her poems, just numbered them. She was quite a curiosity in her town because she only wore white all year long, and would ocassionally bake candies and sweets for the neighborhood children and lower them to the street on a tray attached to a pulley.

Who Are You?

A Poem

by Emily Dickinson

I'm Nobody! Who are you?
Are you—Nobody—Too?
Then there's a pair of us!
Don't tell! they'd advertise—you know!

How dreary—to be—Somebody!
How public—like a Frog—
To tell one's name—the livelong June—
To an admiring Bog!

My Shadow

by Robert Louis Stevenson

I have a little shadow that goes in and out with me,
And what can be the use of him is more than I can see.
He is very, very like me from the heels up to the head;
And I see him jump before me, when I jump into my bed.

The funniest thing about him is the way he likes to grow—
Not at all like proper children, which is always very slow;
For he sometimes shoots up taller like an India-rubber ball,
And he sometimes gets so little that there's none of him at all.

He hasn't got a notion of how children ought to play,
And can only make a fool of me in every sort of way.
He stays so close beside me, he's a coward you can see;
I'd think shame to stick to nursie as that shadow sticks to me!

One morning, very early, before the sun was up,
I rose and found the shining dew on every buttercup;
But my lazy little shadow, like an arrant sleepy-head,
Had stayed at home behind me and was fast asleep in bed.

The funniest thing about him is the way he likes to grow—

Who Are You?

John Kendrick Bangs

John Kendrick Bangs, an American humorist, was born in New York in 1862. He wrote more than 30 books of humorous stories, verse, and plays, and is considered to be an early science fiction writer.

The Little Elf

by John Kendrick Bangs

I met a little Elf-man, once,
Down where the lilies blow.
I asked him why he was so small,
And why he didn't grow.

He slightly frowned, and with his eye
He looked me through and through.
"I'm quite as big for me," said he,
"As you are big for you."

The Raggedy Man

by James Whitcomb Riley

O The Raggedy Man! He works fer Pa;
An' he's the goodest man ever you saw!
He comes to our house every day,
An' waters the horses, an' feeds 'em hay;
An' he opens the shed—an' we all ist laugh
When he drives out our little old wobble-ly calf;
An' nen—ef our hired girls says he can—
He milks the cow fer "Lizabuth Ann.—
Ain't he a' awful good Raggedy Man?
Raggedy! Raggedy! Raggedy Man!

W'y, The Raggedy Man—he's ist so good
He splits the kindlin' an' chops the wood;
An' nen he spades in our garden, too,
An' does most things 'at *boys* can't do!—
He clumbed clean up in our big tree
An' shooked a' apple down fer me—
An' nother'n', too, fer 'Lizabuth Ann—
An' nother'n', too, fer The Raggedy Man.—
Ain't he a' awful kind Raggedy Man?
Raggedy! Raggedy! Raggedy Man!

An' The Raggedy Man, he knows most rhymes
An' tells 'em, ef I be good, sometimes:
Knows 'bout Giunts, an' Griffuns, an' Elves,
An' the Squidgicum-Squees 'at swallers therselves!
An', wite by the pump in our pasture-lot,
He showed me the hole 'at the Wunks is got,
'At lives 'way deep in the ground, an' can
Turn into me, er "Lizabuth Ann,

James Whitcomb Riley

James Whitcomb Riley was born in a log cabin in Indiana in 1849. His parents were afraid he wasn't going to amount to much in life because he couldn't remember history or math. He studied law but wandered around the midwest for a while as a sign painter. Sometimes he traveled from town to town with the "Miracle Medicine Show" and played songs on the violin, banjo, and guitar. His poems were first published in newspapers, and later in beautifully illustrated books. He was given the nickname "The Children's Poet" and eventually became the wealthiest writer of his time.

Who Are You?

Er Ma er Pa er The Raggedy Man!
Ain't he a funny old Raggedy Man?
Raggedy! Raggedy! Raggedy Man!

The Raggedy Man—one time when he
Wuz makin' a little bow-'n'-orry fer me,
Says "When *you're* big like your Pa is,
Air *you* go' to keep a fine store like his—
An' be a rich merchunt—an' wear fine clothes?—
Er what air you go' to be, goodness knows!"
An' nen he laughed at 'Lizabuth Ann,
An' I says "M go' to be a Raggedy Man!—
I'm ist go' to be a nice Raggedy Man!
Raggedy! Raggedy! Raggedy Man!"

Old Woman, Old Woman

a poem from Mother Goose

There was an old woman tossed in a blanket
Seventeen times as high as the moon;
But where she was going no mortal could tell,
For under her arm she carried a broom.

"Old woman, old woman, old woman," said I,
"Whither, oh whither, oh whither so high?"
"To sweep the cobwebs from the sky,
And I'll be with you by and by."

Who was Mother Goose?

Maybe Mother Goose was many she's and he's—different writers—in different times. The first person to use the term "Mother Goose" was Charles Perrault in 1697. His book of eight fairy tales included "The Sleeping Beauty," "Little Red Riding Hood," "Cinderella," "Bluebeard," and others. He called his book **Histories and Tales of Long Ago, with Morals,** *but there was a small subtitle on the cover which read* **Tales of My Mother the Goose.** *Later, John Newberry popularized the name of "Mother Goose" when he published* **Mother Goose's Melody: or Sonnets for the Cradle** *in 1765. The idea of "Mother Goose Rhymes" took hold and they have been popular ever since.*

Who Are You?

Pan's Garden:
Myths

ℰssay

by Dr. Engel

My Old Friend from elementary school science class, the planet Pluto (named for the mythical god of the Dead) has recently been declared dead itself. I find myself to be its chief mourner.

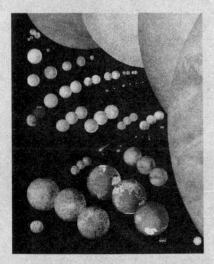

We studied the planets in my fourth-grade class and had to memorize their order from the sun.

Although my academic inclinations have always been with the liberal arts, I've been impressed since elementary school by how much more specific and quantifiable the fields of math and science are. There is something appealing about only one right answer to a math problem and only one correct way to balance a chemical equation. Even the most nebulous concepts in science seem safe from the usual Doubting Thomases. As Albert Einstein cleverly noted: "Tell a man there are three billion stars and he'll believe you. But put a 'wet paint' sign on a park bench and he'll have to touch it—just to be sure."

That is why I find the recent controversy over the status of the planet Pluto so disheartening. Recently astronomers have been trying to decide whether the planet should now be reclassified and downgraded to the status of a mere "trans-Neptunian object." Recently the prestigious Hayden Planetarium in New York removed Pluto from its planetary display. The director explained that Pluto never fit the planetary mold: it's neither rocky like four planets nor gassy like the other four, and its size is even smaller than seven measly moons in the solar system, including Earth's.

We studied the planets in my fourth-grade class and had to memorize their order from the sun. I was enchanted with the phrase that prompted the nine planets in their proper order: **M**y **V**ery **E**ducated **M**other **J**ust **S**erved **U**s **N**ine **P**izzas (Mercury, Venus, Earth, and so on). Now we learn there's no Pizza—No Pluto anymore. Sigh.

I feel for Pluto. As an English professor, I've been witness to this same trendy reclassification—be it upgrading or down—with the stars of the literary firmament. During the nineteenth century Sir Walter Scott was thought to be one of the greatest novelists; today, we note that he is not only unread but virtually unreadable. Edgar Allan Poe's works during most of his lifetime were considered nonsensical and monstrous; today he is in every literary anthology from middle school on and ranked as a baroque genius by most critics.

And, of course, in our own lives people who at first seem to be the very sun of our emotional universe can become nothing more than a comet that blazes and then vanishes. We are constantly relearning the lesson that those who seem an anchor in our lives can sometime be revealed as morally rudderless.

This is the most common theme in literature: appearance versus reality. No writer expressed it more succinctly than Shakespeare. In the tenth line of Macbeth the witches chant: "Fair is foul, and foul is fair." If only we lived in a world where fair always looked fair and foul always appeared foul—indeed where appearance was reality—what a boon it would be for making choices.

But what a loss it would be for literature. Literature must deal with personal morality, the agonizing decisions we all must make that eventually determine the quality of our character. And here the certitudes of science and math are nowhere to be found. But the decisions we make certify whether we shall be remembered like Sydney Carton as a shining star or, like poor Pluto, a demoted luminary.

In the tenth line of Macbeth the witches chant: "Fair is foul, and foul is fair."

Pan's Garden: Myths

Elizabeth Barrett Browning

Elizabeth Barrett Browning was born in 1806 and was the oldest of 12 children. She was very smart and began reading at the age of 4, began writing poems at age 6, and had her first poem published when she was only 12. At age 15, she had a bad accident with her pony "Moses" and had to lie flat on her back for months. She was nicknamed the "Caged Nightingale" because she was confined inside to the couch where she wrote much of her poetry. She later married the famous writer Robert Browning and together they had one son, whom they named "Pen," since both of them were writers.

Pan's Garden: Myths

A Musical Instrument

by Elizabeth Barrett Browning

What was he doing, the great god Pan,
Down in the reeds by the river?
Spreading ruin and scattering ban,
Splashing and paddling with hoofs of a goat,
And breaking the golden lilies afloat
    With the dragon-fly on the river.
He tore out a reed, the great god Pan,
    From the deep cool bed of the river;
The limpid waters turbidly ran,
And the broken lilies a-dying lay,
And the dragon-fly had fled away,
    Ere he brought it out of the river.

He cut it short, did the great god Pan,
    (How tall it stood in the river!)
Then drew the pith, like the heart of a man,
Steadily from the outside ring,
And notched the poor dry empty thing
    In holes, as he sat by the river.

"This is the way," laughed the great god Pan
    (Laughed while he sat by the river),
"The only way, since gods began
To make sweet music, they could succeed."
Then, dropping his mouth to a hole in the reed,
    He blew in power by the river.
Sweet, sweet, sweet, O Pan!

Piercing sweet by the river!
Blinding sweet, O great god Pan!
The sun on the hill forgot to die,
And the lilies revived, and the dragon-fly
     Came back to dream on the river.

Yet half a beast is the great god Pan,
     To laugh as he sits by the river,
Making a poet out of a man.
The true gods sigh for the cost and pain—
For the reed which grows nevermore again
     As a reed with the reeds in the river.

The Golden Touch

by Nathanial Hawthorne

If he loved anything better, or half so well, it was the one little maiden who played so merrily around her father's footstool.

Once upon a time, there lived a very rich man, and a king besides, whose name was Midas; and he had a little daughter, whom nobody but myself ever heard of, and whose name I either never knew, or have entirely forgotten. So, because I love odd names for little girls, I choose to call her Marygold.

This King Midas was fonder of gold than of anything else in the world. He valued his royal crown chiefly because it was composed of that precious metal. If he loved anything better, or half so well, it was the one little maiden who played so merrily around her father's footstool. But the more Midas loved his daughter, the more did he desire and seek for wealth. He thought, foolish man! that the best thing he could possibly do for this dear child would be to bequeath her the immensest pile of yellow, glistening coin, that had ever been heaped together since the world was made. Thus, he gave all his thoughts and all his time to this one purpose. If ever he happened to gaze for an instant at the gold-tinted clouds of sunset, he wished that they were real gold, and that they could be squeezed safely into his strong box. When little Marygold ran to meet him, with a bunch of buttercups and dandelions, he used to say, "Poh, poh, child! If these flowers were as golden as they look, they would be worth the plucking!"

At length (as people always grow more and more foolish, unless they take care to grow wiser and wiser), Midas had got to be so exceedingly unreasonable, that he could scarcely bear to see or touch any object that was not gold. He made it his custom, therefore, to pass a large portion of every day in a dark and dreary apartment, underground, at the basement of his palace. It was here that he kept his wealth. To this dismal hole—for it was little better than a dungeon—Midas betook himself, whenever he wanted to be particularly happy. Here, after carefully locking the door, he would take a bag of gold coin, or a gold cup as big as a washbowl, or a heavy golden bar, or a peck measure of gold dust, and bring them from the obscure corners of the room into the one bright and narrow sunbeam that fell from the dungeon-like window. He valued the sunbeam for no other reason but that his treasure would not shine without its help. And then would he reckon over the coins in the bag; toss up the bar, and catch it as it came down; sift the gold dust through his fingers; look at the funny image of his own face, as reflected in the burnished circumference of the cup; and whisper to himself, "O Midas, rich King Midas, what a happy man art thou!"

Midas called himself a happy man, but felt that he was not yet quite so happy as he might be. The very tiptoe of enjoyment would never be reached, unless the whole world were to become his treasure room, and should be all his own.

Midas was enjoying himself in his treasure room, one day, as usual, when he perceived a shadow fall over the heaps of gold; and, looking suddenly up, what should he behold but the figure of a stranger, standing in the bright and narrow sunbeam! It was a young man, with a cheerful and ruddy face. Whether it was that the imagination of King Midas threw a yellow tinge over everything, or whatever the cause might be, he could not help fancying that the smile with which the stranger regarded him had a kind of golden radiance in it.

Nathaniel Hawthorne

Nathaniel Hawthorne was born in Salem, Massachusetts in 1804. His family name was originally Hathorne, but he added the "w" to it because an early ancestor had been a judge at the Salem witchcraft trials and he was ashamed of having any part in that terrible event in US history. His father was a sea captain who died when Nathaniel was just 3 years old. He and his mother lived with a large extended family and until the time he went away to college, Nathaniel had to share his bedroom with five uncles. His first novel was so bad that he borrowed money to buy all of the published copies and burn them before anyone could read them. Today, he is known for his novel, **The Scarlet Letter**.

Pan's Garden: Myths

As Midas knew that he had carefully turned the key in the lock, and that no mortal strength could possibly break into his treasure room, he, of course, concluded that his visitor must be something more than mortal. It is no matter about telling you who he was. In those days, when the earth was comparatively a new affair, it was supposed to be often the resort of beings endowed with supernatural power, and who used to interest themselves in the joys and sorrows of men, women, and children, half playfully and half seriously. Midas had met such beings before now, and was not sorry to meet one of them again. The stranger's aspect, indeed, was so good-humored and kindly, if not beneficent, that it would have been unreasonable to suspect him of intending any mischief. It was far more probable that he came to do Midas a favor. And what could that favor be, unless to multiply his heaps of treasure?

As Midas knew that he had carefully turned the key in the lock, and that no mortal strength could possible break into his treasure room, he, of course, concluded that his visitor must be something more than mortal.

The stranger gazed upon the room; and when his lustrous smile had glistened upon all the golden objects that were there, he turned again to Midas.

"You are a wealthy man, friend Midas!" he observed. "I doubt whether any other four walls, on earth, contain so much gold as you have contrived to pile up in this room."

"I have done pretty well—pretty well," answered Midas, in a discontented tone. "But, after all, it is but a trifle, when you consider that it has taken me my whole life to get it together. If one could live a thousand years, he might have time to grow rich!"

"What!" exclaimed the stranger. "Then you are not satisfied?"

Midas shook his head.

"And pray what would satisfy you?" asked the stranger. "Merely for the curiosity of the thing, I should be glad to know."

Midas paused and meditated. He felt a presentiment that this stranger, with such a golden luster in his good-humored smile, had come hither with both the power and the purpose of gratifying his utmost wishes. At last, a bright idea occurred to King Midas. It seemed as bright as the glistening metal which he loved so much.

Raising his head, he looked the lustrous stranger in the face.

"Well, Midas," observed his visitor, "I see that you have at length hit upon something that will satisfy you. Tell me your wish."

"It is only this," replied Midas. "I am weary of collecting my treasures with so much trouble, and beholding the heap so diminutive, after I have done my best. I wish everything that I touch to be changed to gold!"

The stranger's smile grew so very broad, that it seemed to fill the room like an outburst of the sun, gleaming into a shadowy dell, where the yellow autumnal leaves—for so looked the lumps and particles of gold—lie strewn in the glow of light.

"The Golden Touch!" exclaimed he. "You certainly deserve credit, friend Midas, for striking out so brilliant a conception. But are you quite sure that this will satisfy you,"

"How could it fail?" said Midas.

"And will you never regret the possession of it?"

"What could induce me?" asked Midas. "I ask nothing else, to render me perfectly happy."

"Be it as you wish, then," replied the stranger, waving his hand in token of farewell. "Tomorrow, at sunrise, you will find yourself gifted with the Golden Touch."

The figure of the stranger then became exceedingly bright, and Midas involuntarily closed his eyes. On

"It is only this," replied Midas. "I am weary of collecting my treasures with so much trouble, and beholding the heap so diminutive, after I have done my best, I wish everything that I touch to be changed to gold!"

opening them again, he beheld only one yellow sunbeam in the room, and, all around him, the glistening of the precious metal which he had spent his life in hoarding up.

Day had hardly peeped over the hills, when King Midas was broad awake, and, stretching his arms out of bed, began to touch the objects that were within reach. He was anxious to prove whether the Golden Touch had really come, according to the stranger's promise. So he laid his finger on a chair by the bedside, and on various other things, but was grievously disappointed to perceive that they remained exactly the same substances as before. Indeed, he felt very much afraid that he had only dreamed about the lustrous stranger, or else that the latter had been making game of him.

All this while, it was only the gray of the morning, with but a streak of brightness along the edge of the sky, where Midas could not see it. He lay in a very disconsolate mood, regretting the downfall of his hopes, and kept growing sadder and sadder, until the earliest sunbeam shone through the window, and gilded the ceiling over this head. It seemed to Midas that this bright yellow sunbeam was reflected in rather a singular way on the white covering of the bed. Looking more closely, what was his astonishment and delight, when he found that this linen fabric had been transmuted to what seemed a woven texture of the purest and brightest gold! The Golden Touch had come to him with the first sunbeam!

Midas started up, in a kind of joyful frenzy, and ran about the room, grasping at everything that happened to be in his way. He seized one of the bedposts, and it became immediately a fluted golden pillar. He took up a book from the table. At his first touch, it assumed the appearance of such a splendidly bound and gilt-edged

Day had hardly peeped over the hills, when King Midas was broad awake, and, stretching his arms out of bed, began to touch the objects that were within reach.

volume as one often meets with, nowadays; but on running his fingers through the leaves, behold! it was a bundle of thin golden plates, in which all the wisdom of the book had grown illegible. He hurriedly put on his clothes, and was enraptured to see himself in a magnificent suit of gold cloth, which retained its flexibility and softness, although it burdened him a little with its weight. He drew out his handkerchief, which little Marygold had hemmed for him. That was likewise gold, with the dear child's neat and pretty stitches running all along the border, in gold thread!

Somehow or other, this last transformation did not quite please King Midas. He would rather that his little daughter's handiwork should have remained just the same as when she climbed his knee and put it into his hand.

But it was not worthwhile to vex himself about a trifle. Midas now took his spectacles from this pocket, and put them on his nose, in order that he might see more distinctly what he was about.

To his great perplexity, however, excellent as the glasses were, he discovered that he could not see through them. But this was the most natural thing in the world; for, on taking them off, the transparent crystal turned out to be plates of yellow metal, and, of course, were worthless as spectacles, though valuable as gold. It struck Midas as rather inconvenient that, with all his wealth, he could never again be rich enough to own a pair of serviceable spectacles.

"It is no great matter, nevertheless," said he to himself, very philosophically. "We cannot expect any great good, without its being accompanied with some small inconvenience. The Golden Touch is worth the sacrifice of a pair of spectacles, at least, if not of one's very eyesight. My own eyes will serve for ordinary

He hurriedly put on his clothes, and was enraptured to see himself in a magnificent suit of gold cloth.

So he took great pains in going from bush to bush, and exercised his magic touch most indefatigably; until every individual flower and bud, and even the worms at the heart of some of them, were changed to gold.

purposes, and little Marygold will soon be old enough to read to me."

Wise King Midas was so exalted by his good fortune, that the palace seemed not sufficiently spacious to contain him. He lifted the door latch (it was brass only a moment ago, but golden when his fingers quitted it), and emerged into the garden. Here, as it happened, he found a great number of beautiful roses in full bloom and others in all the stages of lovely bud and blossom. Very delicious was their fragrance in the morning breeze. Their delicate blush was one of the fairest sights in the world; so gentle, so modest, and so full of sweet tranquility, did these roses seem to be.

But Midas knew a way to make them far more precious, according to his way of thinking, than roses had ever been before. So he took great pains in going from bush to bush, and exercised his magic touch most indefatigably; until every individual flower and bud, and even the worms at the heart of some of them, were changed to gold. By the time this good work was completed, King Midas was summoned to breakfast; and as the morning air had given him an excellent appetite, he made haste back to the palace.

Little Marygold had not yet made her appearance. Her father ordered her to be called and seating himself at the table awaited the child's coming, in order to begin his own breakfast. To do Midas justice, he really loved his daughter, and loved her so much the more this morning, on account of the good fortune which had befallen him. It was not a great while before he heard her coming along the passageway crying bitterly. This circumstance surprised him, because Marygold was one of the cheerfullest little people whom you would see in a summer's day, and hardly shed a thimbleful of tears in a twelve-month. When Midas heard her sobs, he determined to put little Marygold into better spirits, by an agreeable surprise, so leaning across the table, he touched his daughter's bowl (which was a China one, with pretty figures around it), and transmuted it to gleaming gold.

Meanwhile, Marygold slowly and disconsolately opened the door, and showed herself with her apron at her eyes, still sobbing as if her heart would break.

"How now, my little lady!" cried Midas. "Pray what is the matter with you, this bright morning?"

Marygold, without taking the apron from her eyes, held out her hand, in which was one of the roses which Midas had so recently transmuted.

"Beautiful!" exclaimed her father. "And what is there in this magnificent golden rose to make you cry?"

"Ah, dear father!" answered the child, as well as her sobs would let her; "it is not beautiful, but the ugliest flower that ever grew!

"As soon as I was dressed I ran into the garden to gather some roses for you; because I know you like them, and like them the better when gathered by your little daughter. But, oh dear, dear me! What do you think as happened? Such a misfortune! All the beautiful roses, that smelled so sweetly and had so many lovely blushes, are blighted and spoilt! They are grown quite yellow, as you see this one, and have no longer any fragrance! What can have been the matter with them?"

"Poh, my dear little girl—pray don't cry about it!" said Midas, who was ashamed to confess that he himself had wrought the change which so greatly afflicted her. "Sit down and eat your bread and milk! You will find it easy enough to exchange a golden rose like that (which will last hundreds of years) for an ordinary one which would wither in a day."

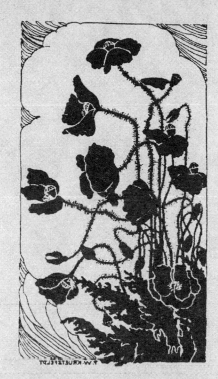

"Ah, dear father!" answered the child, as well as her sobs would let her; "it is not beautiful, but the ugliest flower that ever grew!"

Pan's Garden: Myths

"I don't care for such roses as this!" cried Marygold, tossing it contemptuously away. "It has no smell, and the hard petals prick my nose!"

The child now sat down to table, but was so occupied with her grief for the blighted roses that she did not even notice the wonderful transmutation of her China bowl. Perhaps this was all better; for Marygold was accustomed to take pleasure in looking at the queer figures, and strange trees and places, that were painted on the circumference of the bowl; and these ornaments were now entirely lost in the yellow hue of the metal.

Midas, meanwhile, had poured out a cup of coffee, and, as a matter of course, the coffeepot, whatever metal it may have been when he took it up, was gold when he set it down. He thought to himself, that it was rather an extravagant style of splendor, in a king of his simple habits, to breakfast off a service of gold, and began to be puzzled with the difficulty of keeping his treasures safe. The cupboard and the kitchen would no longer be a secure place of deposit for articles so valuable as golden bowls and coffeepots.

Amid these thoughts, he lifted a spoonful of coffee to his lips, and, sipping it, was astonished to perceive that, the instant his lips touched the liquid, it became molten gold, and the next moment, hardened into a lump! "Ha!" exclaimed Midas, rather aghast.

"What is the matter, father?" asked little Marygold, gazing at him, with the tears still standing in her eyes.

"Nothing, child, nothing!" said Midas. "Eat your breakfast, before it gets quite cold."

He took one of the nice little trouts on his plate, and, by way of experiment, touched its tail with his finger. To his horror, it was immediately transmuted from an admirably fried brook trout into a gold fish,

Midas, meanwhile, had poured out a cup of coffee, and, as a matter of course, the coffeepot, whatever metal it may have been when he took it up, was gold when he set it down.

though not one of those goldfishes which people often keep in glass globes, as ornaments for the parlor. No; but it was really a metallic fish, and looked as if it had been very cunningly made by the nicest goldsmith in the world. Its little bones were now golden wires; its fins and tail were thin plates of gold; and there were the marks of the fork in it, and all the delicate, frothy appearance of a nicely fried fish, exactly imitated in metal. A very pretty piece of work, as you may suppose; only King Midas, just at the moment, would much rather have had a real trout in his dish that this elaborate and valuable imitation of one.

"I don't quite see," thought he to himself, "how I am to get any breakfast."

Almost in despair; he helped himself to a boiled egg, which immediately underwent a change similar to that of the trout. The egg, indeed, might have been mistaken for one of those which the famous goose, in the storybook, was in the habit of laying; but King Midas was the only goose that had anything to do with the matter.

"Well, this is a quandary!" thought he, leaning back in his chair, and looking quite enviously at little Marygold, who was now eating her bread and milk with great satisfaction. "Such a costly breakfast before me, and nothing that can be eaten!"

Hoping that, by dint of great dispatch, he might avoid what he now felt to be a considerable inconvenience, King Midas next snatched a hot potato, and attempted to cram it into his mouth, and swallow it in a hurry. But the Golden Touch was too nimble for him. He found his mouth full, not of mealy potato but of solid metal, which so burnt his tongue that he roared aloud, and, jumping up from the table, began to dance and stamp about the room both with pain and affright.

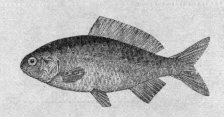

. . . but it was really a metallic fish, and looked as if it had been very cunningly made by the nicest goldsmith in the world.

Pan's Garden: Myths

The poorest laborer, sitting down to his crust of bread and cup of water, was far better off than King Midas, whose delicate food was really worth its weight in gold.

"Father, dear father!" cried little Marygold, who was a very affectionate child, "pray what is the matter? Have you burnt your mouth?"

"Ah, dear child," groaned Midas, dolefully, "I don't know what is to become of your poor father!"

The poorest laborer, sitting down to his crust of bread and cup of water, was far better off than King Midas, whose delicate food was really worth its weight in gold. And what was to be done? Already, at breakfast, Midas was excessively hungry. Would he be less so by dinnertime? And how ravenous would be his appetite for supper, which must undoubtedly consist of the same sort of indigestible dishes as those now before him! How many days, think you, would he survive a continuance of this rich fare?

These reflections so troubled wise King Midas, that he began to doubt whether, after all, riches are the one desirable thing in the world, or even the most desirable. But this was only a passing thought. So fascinated was Midas with the glitter of the yellow metal, that he would still have refused to give up the Golden Touch for so paltry a consideration as breakfast.

"It would be quite too dear," thought Midas.

Nevertheless, so great was his hunger, and the perplexity of his situation, that he again groaned aloud, and very grievously too. Our pretty Marygold could endure it no longer. She sat, a moment, gazing at her father, and trying, with all the might of her little wits, to find out what was the matter with him. Then, with a sweet and sorrowful impulse to comfort him, she started from her chair, and, running to Midas threw her arms affectionately about his knees. He bent down and kissed her. He felt that his little daughter's love was worth a thousand times more than the Golden Touch.

"My precious, precious, Marygold!" cried he.

But Marygold made no answer.

Alas, what had he done? How fatal was the gift which the stranger bestowed! The moment the lips of Midas touched Marygold's forehead, a change had taken place. Her sweet, rosy face, so full of affection as it had been, assumed a glittering yellow color, with yellow teardrops congealing on her cheeks. Her beautiful brown ringlets took the same tint. Her soft and tender little form grew hard and inflexible within her father's encircling arms. Oh, terrible misfortune! The victim of his insatiable desire for wealth, little Marygold was a human child no longer, but a golden statue!

Yes, there she was, with the questioning look of love, grief, and pity, hardened into her face. It was the prettiest and most woeful sight that every mortal saw. All the features and tokens of Marygold were there; even the beloved little dimple remained in her golden chin. But the more perfect was the resemblance, the greater was the father's agony at beholding this golden image, which was all that was left him of a daughter. It had been a favorite phrase of Midas, whenever he felt particularly fond of the child, to say that she was worth her weight in gold. And now the phrase had become literally true. And now, at last, when it was too late, he felt how infinitely a warm and tender heart, that loved him, exceeding in value all the wealth that could be piled up betwixt the earth and sky!

It would be too sad a story, if I were to tell you how Midas, in the fullness of all his gratified desires, began to wring his hands and bemoan himself; and how he could neither bear to look at Marygold, nor yet to look away from her. Except when his eyes were fixed on the image, he could not possibly believe that she had been changed to gold.

But the more perfect was the resemblance, the greater was the father's agony at beholding this golden image, which was all that was left him of a daughter.

Pan's Garden: Myths

. . . he recognized the same figure which had appeared to him, the day before, in the treasure room, and had bestowed on him this disastrous faculty of the Golden Touch.

But, stealing another glance, there was the precious little figure, with a yellow teardrop on its yellow cheek, and a look so piteous and tender, that it seemed as if that very expression must needs soften the gold, and make it flesh again. This, however, could not be. So Midas had only to wring his hands, and to wish that he were the poorest man in the wide world, if the loss of all his wealth might bring back the faintest rose color to his dear child's face.

While he was in this tumult of despair, he suddenly beheld a stranger standing near the door. Midas bent down his head, without speaking; for he recognized the same figure which had appeared to him, the day before, in the treasure room, and had bestowed on him this disastrous faculty of the Golden Touch. The stranger's countenance still wore a smile, which seemed to shed a yellow luster all about the room, and gleamed on little Marygold's image, and on the other objects that had been transmuted by the touch of Midas.

"Well, friend Midas," said the stranger, "pray how do you succeed with the Golden Touch?"

"I am very miserable," said he.

"Very miserable, indeed!" exclaimed the stranger. "And how happens that? Have I not faithfully kept my promise with you? Have you not everything that your heart desired?"

"Gold is not everything," answered Midas. "And I have lost all that my heart really cared for."

"Ah, So you have made a discovery, since yesterday?" observed the stranger. "Let us see, then. Which of these two things do you think is really worth the most—the gift of the Golden Touch, or one cup of clear cold water?"

"O blessed water!" exclaimed Midas. "It will never moisten my parched throat again!"

"The Golden Touch," continued the stranger, "or a crust of bread?"

"The Golden Touch," asked the stranger, "or your own little Marygold, warm, soft, and loving as she was an hour ago?"

"Oh, my child, my dear child!" cried poor Midas, wringing his hands. "I would not have given that one small dimple in her chin for the power of changing this whole earth into a solid lump of gold!"

"You are wiser than you were, King Midas!" said the stranger, looking seriously at him. "Your own heart, I perceive, has not been entirely changed from flesh to gold. Were it so, your case would indeed be desperate. But you appear to be still capable of understanding that the commonest things, such as lie within everyone's grasp, are more valuable than the riches which so many mortals sigh and struggle after. Tell me, do you sincerely desire to rid yourself of this Golden Touch?"

"It is hateful to me!" replied Midas.

A fly settled on his nose, but immediately fell to the floor, for it, too, had become gold. Midas shuddered.

"Go, then," said the stranger, "and plunge into the river that glides past the bottom of your garden. Take likewise a vase of the same water, and sprinkle it over any object that you may desire to change back again from gold into its former substance. If you do this in earnestness and sincerity, it may possibly repair the mischief which your avarice has occasioned."

King Midas bowed low; and when he lifted his head the lustrous stranger had vanished.

You will easily believe that Midas lost no time in snatching up a great earthen pitcher (but, alas me! it was no longer earthen after he touched it), and hastening to the riverside. As he scampered along, and

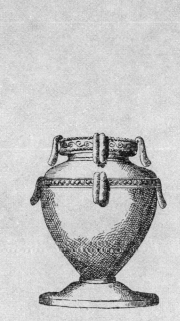

Take likewise a vase of the same water, and sprinkle it over any object that you may desire to change back again from gold into its former substance.

No sooner did it fall on her than you would have laughed to see how the rosy color came back to the dear child's cheek!

forced his way through the shrubbery, it was positively marvelous to see how the foliage turned yellow behind him, as if the autumn had been there, and nowhere else. On reaching the river's brink, he plunged headlong in, without waiting so much as to pull off his shoes.

As he dipped the pitcher into the water, it gladdened his very heart to see it change from gold into the same good, honest, earthen vessel which it had been before he touched it. He was conscious, also, of a change within himself. A cold, hard, and heavy weight seemed to have gone out of his bosom.

No doubt, his heart had been gradually losing its human substance, and transmuting itself into insensible metal, but had now softened back again into flesh. Perceiving a violet that grew on the bank of the river Midas touched it with his finger, and was overjoyed to find the delicate flower retained its purple hue, instead of undergoing a yellow blight. The curse of the Golden Touch had, therefore, really been removed from him.

King Midas hastened back to the palace; and, I suppose, the servants knew not what to make of it when they saw their royal master so carefully bringing home an earthen pitcher of water. But that water, which was to undo all the mischief that his folly had wrought, was more precious to Midas than an ocean of molten gold could have been. The first thing he did, as you need hardly be told, was to sprinkle handfuls over the golden figure of little Marygold.

No sooner did it fall on her than you would have laughed to see how the rosy color came back to the dear child's cheek! and how she began to sneeze and sputter!—and how astonished she was to find herself dripping wet, and her father still throwing more water over her!

"Pray do not, dear father!" cried she. "See how you have wet my nice frock, which I put on only this morning!"

For Marygold did not know that she had been a little golden statue; nor could she remember anything that had happened since the moment when she ran with outstretched arms to comfort poor King Midas.

Her father did not think it necessary to tell his beloved child how very foolish he had been, but contented himself with showing how much wiser he had grown. For this purpose, he led little Marygold into the garden, where he sprinkled all the remainder of the water over the rose bushes, and with such good effect that above five thousand roses recovered their beautiful bloom. There were two circumstances, however, which, as long as he lived, used to put King Midas in mind of the Golden Touch. One was, that the sands of the river sparkled like gold; the other, the little Marygold's hair had now a golden tinge, which he had never observed in it before she had been transmuted by the effect of his kiss.

When King Midas had grown quite an old man, and used to trot Marygold's children on his knee, he was fond of telling them this marvelous story, pretty much as I have now told it to you. And then would he stroke their glossy ringlets, and tell them that their hair, likewise, had a rich shade of gold, which they had inherited from their mother.

"And to tell you the truth, my precious little folks," quoth King Midas, diligently trotting the children all the while," ever since that morning, I have hated the very sight of all other gold, save this!"

For this purpose, he led little Marygold into the garden, where he sprinkled all the remainder of the water over the rose bushes, and with such good effect that above five thousand roses recovered their beautiful bloom.

Aesop

Aesop was a Greek slave who was born about 3000 years ago. Aesop's stories are called fables, simple tales intended to convey a certain moral or truth. Aesop never wrote down any of these stories—he told them to people, who told them to other people. His talent for entertaining people was so great that he eventually won his freedom and was made an advisor to kings. He was on a peace-making mission to Delphi, Greece, for King Croesus when he was killed by angry citizens. It was not until 200 years after his death that the first collection of his famous fables appeared. Since then they have been translated into almost every language in the world.

Pan's Garden: Myths

The Fox and the Grapes

by Aesop

One hot summer's day a fox was strolling through an orchard till he came to a bunch of grapes just ripening on a vine which had been trained over a lofty branch. "Just the thing to quench my thirst," quoth he. Drawing back a few paces, he took a run and a jump, and just missed the bunch. Turning round again with a one, two, three, he jumped up, but with no greater success. Again and again he tried after the tempting morsel, but at last had to give it up, and walked away with his nose in the air, saying: I am sure they are sour."

It is easy to despise what you cannot get.

This old myth is the story of winter and summer, of the grains maturing below ground in darkness.

The Age of Fable

Mythology is the handmaid of literature; and literature is one of the best allies of virtue and promoters of happiness. Without a knowledge of mythology much of the elegant literature of our own language cannot be understood and appreciated. We are indebted to the ancient Greeks and Romans for this wonderful gift to us.

Proserpine

from The Age of Fable

When Jupiter and his brothers had defeated the Titans and banished them to Tartarus, a new enemy rose up against the gods. They were the giants Typhon, Briareus, Enceladus, and others. Some of them had a hundred arms, others breathed out fire. They were finally subdued and buried alive under Mount Aetna, where they still sometimes get loose, and shake the whole island with earthquakes. Their breath comes up through the mountain, and is what men call the eruption of the volcano.

The fall of these monsters shook the earth, so that Pluto was alarmed, and feared that his kingdom would be laid open to the light of day. Under this apprehension, he mounted his chariot, drawn by black horses, and took a circuit of inspection to satisfy himself of the extent of the damage.

While he was thus engaged, Venus, who was sitting on Mount Eryx playing with her boy Cupid, espied him, and said, "My son, take your darts with which you conquer all, even Jove himself, and send one into the breast of yonder dark monarch, who rules the realm of Tartarus. Why should he alone escape? Seize the opportunity to extend your empire and mine. Do you not see that even in heaven some despise our power? Minerva the wise, and Diana the huntress, defy us; and there is that daughter of Ceres, who threatens to follow their example. Now do you, if you have any regard for your own interest or mine, join these two in one."

The boy unbound his quiver, and selected his

sharpest and truest arrow; then, straining the bow against his knee, he attached the string, and, having made ready, shot the arrow with its barbed point right into the heart of Pluto.

In the vale of Enna there is a lake embowered in woods, which screen it from the fervid rays of the sun, while the moist ground is covered with flowers, and Spring reigns perpetual. Here Proserpine was playing with her companions, gathering lilies and violets, and filling her basket and her apron with them, when Pluto saw her, loved her, and carried her off. She screamed for help to her mother and her companions; and when in her fright she dropped the corners of her apron and let the flowers fall, childlike she felt the loss of them as an addition to her grief. The ravisher urged on his steeds, calling them each by name, and throwing loose over their heads and necks his iron-colored reins. When he reached the River Cyane, and it opposed his passage, he struck the riverbank with his trident, and the earth opened and gave him a passage to Tartarus.

Ceres sought her daughter all the world over. Bright-haired Aurora, when she came forth in the morning, and Hesperus, when he led out the stars in the evening, found her still busy in the search. But it was all unavailing. At length weary and sad, she sat down upon a stone, and continued sitting nine days and nights, in the open air, under the sunlight and moonlight and falling showers. It was where now stands the city of Eleusis, then the home of an old man named Celeus. He was out in the field, gathering acorns and blackberries, and sticks for his fire. His little girl was driving home their two goats, and as she passed the goddess, who appeared in the guise of an old woman, she said to her, "Mother,"—and the

. . . Proserpine was playing with her companions, gathering lilies and violets, and filling her basket and her apron with them . . .

Pan's Garden: Myths

name was sweet to the ears of Ceres,—"why do you sit here alone upon the rocks?"

The old man also stopped, though his load was heavy, and begged her to come into his cottage, such as it was. She declined, and he urged her.

"Go in peace," she replied, "and be happy in your daughter; I have lost mine." As she spoke, tears—something gods never weep,—fell down her cheeks upon her bosom.

The compassionate old man and his child wept with her. Then said he, "Come with us, and despise not our humble roof; so may your daughter be restored to you in safety."

"Lead on," said she, "I cannot resist that appeal!" So she rose from the stone and went with them.

As they walked he told her that his only son, a little boy, lay very sick, feverish and sleepless. She stooped and gathered some poppies. As they entered the cottage, they found all in great distress, for the boy seemed past the hope of recovery. Metanira, his mother, received her kindly, and the goddess stooped and kissed the lips of the sick child. Instantly, the paleness left his face, and healthy vigor returned to his body.

The whole family were delighted—that is, the father, mother, and little girl, for they were all; they had no servants. They spread the table, and put upon it curds and cream, apples, and honey in the comb. While they ate, Ceres mingled poppy juice in the milk of the boy. When night came and all was still, she arose, and taking the sleeping boy, moulded his limbs with her hands, and uttered over him three times a solemn charm, then went and laid him in the ashes. His mother, who had been watching what her guest was doing, sprang forward with a cry and snatched

Then said he, "Come with us, and despise not our humble roof; so may your daughter be restored to you in safety."

the child from the fire. Then Ceres assumed her own form, and a divine splendor shone all around.

While they were overcome with astonishment, she said, "Mother, you have been cruel in your fondness to your son. I would have made him immortal, but you have frustrated my attempt. Nevertheless, he shall be great and useful. He shall teach men the use of the plough, and the rewards which labor can win from the cultivated soil." So saying, she wrapped a cloud about her, and mounting her chariot rode away.

Ceres continued her search for her daughter, passing from land to land, and across seas and rivers, till at length she returned to Sicily, whence she at first set out, and stood by the banks of the River Cyane, where Pluto made himself a passage with his prize to his own dominions. The river nymph would have told the goddess all she had witnessed, but dared not, for fear of Pluto; so she only ventured to take up the girdle which Proserpine had dropped in her flight, and waft it to the feet of the mother. Ceres, seeing this, was no longer in doubt of her loss, but she did not yet know the cause, and laid the blame on the innocent land.

"Ungrateful sorrow," said she, "which I have endowed with fertility and clothed with herbage and nourishing grain, no more shall you enjoy my favors."

Then the cattle died, the plough broke in the furrow, the seed failed to come up; there was too much sun, there was too much rain; the birds stole the seeds—thistles and brambles were the only growth.

Seeing this, the fountain Arethusa interceded for the land. "Goddess," said she, "blame not the land; it opened unwillingly to yield a passage to your

Ceres continued her search for her daughter, passing from land to land, and across seas and rivers. . .

When Ceres heard this, she stood for a while stupefied. . .

daughter. I can tell you of her fate, for I have seen her…. While I passed through the lower parts of the earth, I saw your Proserpine. She was sad, but no longer showing alarm in her countenance. Her look was such as became a queen—the queen of Erebus; the powerful bride of the monarch of the realms of the dead."

When Ceres heard this, she stood for a while stupefied; then turned her chariot towards heaven, and hastened to present herself before the throne of Jove. She told the story of her bereavement, and implored Jupiter to interfere to procure the restitution of her daughter. Jupiter consented on one condition, namely, that Proserpine should not during her stay in the lower world have taken any food; otherwise, the Fates forbade her release. Accordingly, Mercury was sent, accompanied by Spring, to demand Proserpine of Pluto. The wily monarch consented; but alas! The maiden had taken a pomegranate which Pluto offered her, and had sucked the sweet pulp from a few of the seeds. This was enough to prevent her complete release; but a compromise was made, by which she was to pass half the time with her mother, and the rest with her husband Pluto.

Ceres allowed herself to be pacified with this arrangement, and restored the earth to her favor. Now she remembered Celeus and his family, and her promise to his infant son Triptolemus. When the boy grew up, she taught him the use of the plough, and how to sow the seed. She took him in her chariot, drawn by winged dragons, through all the countries of the earth, imparting to mankind valuable grains, and the knowledge of agriculture. After his return, Triptolemus built a magnificent temple to Ceres in

Eleusis, and established the worship of the goddess, under the name of the Eleusinian mysteries, which, in the splendor and solemnity of their observance, surpassed all other religious celebrations among the Greeks.

Shivers—
Tales of Terror

Even though I only met my Hungarian cousin once, his inimitable spirit has been a sustaining Old Friend to all of us fortunate enough to call him family.

Essay

by Dr. Engel

I believe that Charles Dickens would have been pleased that the movie *Schindler's List* won seven Academy Awards. Its two major themes were Dickens' as well. As a shrewd literary critic once observed, Dickens' second most pervasive theme was man's inhumanity to man; but, ironically, his most pervasive theme was man's humanity toward his fellow man. As with Spielberg's movie, Dickens' works had the uncanny ability to anger his audience with tales of greed and corruption yet simultaneously inspire with acts of individual heroism within such a wicked world.

Dickens' heart would have especially ached for the plight of the children during the Holocaust. As a champion of the mistreated child, he would have been horrified by the Nazi's wholesale destruction of so many young lives. Recently, numerous exhibits have focused on "The Children of the Holocaust." Although it seems almost sacrilege for me to write this, I, too—in a minuscule way—have felt in one sense like a child of the Holocaust.

Let me explain. I grew up in a traditional Jewish home in Indianapolis following World War II. The Nazi atrocities were made real to me at a very early age because of my father's family. My father had been born in Hungary but left when he was eleven in 1923. Although his immediate family was in America long before Hitler came to power, his more distant cousins and other relatives perished during the Nazi occupation of Hungary in 1944. Of our 102 family members there, 98 were killed.

And so during the 1950s I vividly remember as a child attending many programs about the Holocaust, some of them featuring those horrific movies made by the troops who liberated the concentration camps. Since Indianapolis had a small Jewish population for a city its size, we would see the same Jewish families at all these lectures. My father once sardonically noted that the very people who needed to be educated to the Holocaust were never at these programs; only the Jewish population—who knew all too well what had happened—could be counted on for faithful attendance.

Of our four Hungarian relatives who survived, I want to introduce you to one—my remarkable cousin Armin Kolar. Here was a man whom Charles Dickens could have created. For in the purely evil world of the Nazis, his inimitable spirit not only triumphed but also assured his survival.

Armin was a most devoted husband and a doting father to his daughter. When the Nazis invaded Hungary, the three of them were loaded onto a train whose destination was a Polish concentration camp. By 1944, most Jews realized that they were being sent to their deaths. Families on the train were separated; Armin rode in one car with the older men; his wife and daughter were in another. As the train pulled out of the station, Armin felt a razor blade in his pocket. A more selfish and pessimistic man might have thought of it as a method of suicide and thus an escape from the horrors which awaited him. But Armin would never have deserted his cherished wife and daughter. As the hellish train ride began, he decided to use the razor to shave off the scraggly beard and moustache he had grown during the previous weeks of Nazi occupation. It was a slow and painstaking process to attempt to shave with one dull razor on that claustrophobic and jarring

What was Schindler's List?

In 1944, when the Nazis demanded the labor camps be closed as part of their "Final Solution," targeting all Jews to be sent to Auschwitz, Gross-Rosen or Treblinka extermination camps, Oscar Schindler used his resourcefulness to try to save his people. Speed was vital: any delays could send his workers up the chimneys. He capitalized on his skillfully cultivated Nazi connections. He would be allowed to draw up a list of "essential" Jewish workers whom he could take with him as his work force. When word spread that there was a list, everyone prayed to be on it. Schindler drafted a list of over 1,000 names. On May 7, 1945, Schindler's Jews learned the news of Germany's surrender. The war would end at midnight. Schindler already knew the Russians were about to enter Brinnlitz, and knew he had to avoid them and reach the Americans. It was painful and agonizing for his workers to say goodbye. Before his departure, his Jews presented him with a gift — a ring they had made from gold extracted from one of his worker's teeth. They had inscribed on it the Talmudic verse:

"Whoever saves one life, saves the world entire."

train.

And it seemed a rather ludicrous act, given the graveness of his situation. But Armin told us later that he did it because if he were lucky enough to spot his beloved wife and daughter when they all left the train, he wanted them to see him one last time looking as dapper and fresh as possible. Perhaps, he thought, it would lift their spirits and make them smile.

When the train finally pulled into the concentration camp after the horrible two-day ride, Armin was indeed a striking contrast to the other men in the car. Armin's countenance was both clean-shaven and refreshed. Little did he realize that his barbering would save his life. For immediately upon exiting the train, Nazi doctors examined each person and, in a moment, decided if the victim was too old for hard labor and therefore should be sent to the gas chambers immediately. Armin was already in his late 50s but because of the shave he appeared much younger. He was spared. His close shave—as he would joke later— was indeed a close shave in both senses of the word.

The three of them were separated during their months in the camp, but miraculously, they all survived. They had no Oscar Schindler to put them on his list of life, but Armin's indomitable personality protected him just as well. Perhaps we are to view that list of Oscar Schindler's as a metaphor for the human spirit of goodness and self-sacrifice that has given succor to victims of persecution throughout history.

If so, then that list serves as a companion symbol to John Donne's bell. You may remember that Donne, the seventeenth-century poet, once wrote concerning the tolling of the death knell: "Never send to know for whom the bell tolls; it tolls for thee." In that same inclusive spirit, we should not ask whose names were on Schindler's list. For the list is not Schindler's—it is ours. And as Dickens taught us in his novels, we must place all humanity on it and then, like Schindler, pay it every kind of service—except that of our lip.

The Tell-Tale Heart

by Edgar Allan Poe

And every night, about midnight, I turned the latch of his door and opened it— oh, so gently!

True!—nervous—very, very dreadfully nervous I had been and am; but why will you say that I am mad? The disease had sharpened my senses—not destroyed—not dulled them. Above all was the sense of hearing acute. I heard all things in the heaven and in the earth. I heard many things in hell. How, then, am I mad? Hearken! and observe how healthily—how calmly I can tell you the whole story.

It is impossible to say how first the idea entered my brain; but once conceived, it haunted me day and night. Object there was none. Passion there was none. I loved the old man. He had never wronged me. He had never given me insult. For his gold I had no desire. I think it was his eye! yes, it was this! He had the eye of a vulture—a pale blue eye, with a film over it. Whenever it fell upon me, my blood ran cold; and so by degrees— very gradually—I made up my mind to take the life of the old man, and thus rid myself of the eye forever.

Now this is the point. You fancy me mad. Madmen know nothing. But you should have seen me. You should have seen how wisely I proceeded—with what caution—with what foresight—with what dissimulation I went to work! I was never kinder to the old man than during the whole week before I killed him. And every night, about midnight, I turned the latch of his door and opened it—oh, so gently! And then, when I had made an opening sufficient for my head, I put in a dark lantern, all closed, closed, so that no light shone out, and then I thrust in my head. Oh, you would have laughed to see how cunningly I thrust it in! I moved it slowly—very, very slowly, so that I might not disturb the old man's sleep. It took me an hour to place my whole head within the opening so far that I could see him as he lay upon his bed. Ha!—would a madman have been so wise as this? And then, when my head was well in the room, I undid the lantern cautiously—oh, so cautiously—cautiously (for the hinges creaked)—I undid it just so much that a single thin ray fell upon the vulture eye. And this I did for seven long nights—every night just at midnight—but I found the eye always closed; and so it was impossible to do the work; for it was not the old man who vexed me, but his Evil Eye. And every morning, when the day broke, I went boldly into the chamber, and spoke courageously to him, calling him by name in a hearty tone, and inquiring how he had passed the night. So you see he would have been a very profound old man, indeed, to suspect that every night, just at twelve, I looked in upon him while he slept.

Upon the eighth night I was more than usually cautious in opening the door. A watch's minute hand moves more quickly than did mine. Never before that night, had I felt the extent of my own powers—of my sagacity. I could scarcely contain my feelings of triumph. To think that there I was, opening the door, little by little, and he not even to dream of my secret deeds or thoughts. I fairly chuckled at the idea; and perhaps he heard me; for he moved on the bed suddenly, as if startled. Now you may think that I drew back—but no. His room was as black as pitch with the thick darkness (for the shutters were close fastened, through fear of robbers), and so I knew that he could not see the opening of the door, and I kept pushing it on steadily, steadily.

I had my head in, and was about to open the

Edgar Allan Poe

Edgar Allan Poe was born in Richmond, Virginia, in 1809. His mother was a child star actress and his father was a sensational dancer. Being poor and unable to afford a babysitter, they put young Edgar in the front row of the theater every evening where he watched his mother "die" a tragic death in her performance. Many scholars feel this was a crucial event in his early development that led to his bizarre and unusual life. Poe died at the early age of 40 under mysterious circumstances and is buried in Westminster Graveyard in Baltimore, Maryland.

lantern, when my thumb slipped upon the tin fastening, and the old man sprang up in bed, crying out—"Who's there?"

I kept quite still and said nothing. For a whole hour I did not move a muscle, and in the meantime I did not hear him lie down. He was still sitting up in the bed listening;—just as I have done, night after night, hearkening to the deathwatches in the wall.

Presently I heard a slight groan, and I knew it was the groan of mortal terror. It was not a groan of pain or of grief—oh, no!—it was the low stifled sound that arises from the bottom of the soul when overcharged with awe. I knew the sound well. Many a night, just at midnight, when all the world slept, it has welled up from my own bosom, deepening, with its dreadful echo, the terrors that distracted me. I say I knew it well. I knew what the old man felt, and pitied him, although I chuckled at heart. I knew that he had been lying awake ever since the first slight noise, when he had turned in the bed. His fears had been ever since growing upon him. He had been trying to fancy them causeless, but could not. He had been saying to himself—"It is nothing but the wind in the chimney— it is only a mouse crossing the floor," or "It is merely a cricket which has made a single chirp." Yes, he had been trying to comfort himself with these suppositions; but he had found all in vain. All in vain; because Death, in approaching him had stalked with his black shadow before him, and enveloped the victim. And it was the mournful influence of the unperceived shadow that caused him to feel—although he neither saw nor heard—to feel the presence of my head within the room.

When I had waited a long time, very patiently, without hearing him lie down, I resolved to open a little—a very, very little crevice in the lantern. So I

He was still sitting up in the bed listening;—just as I have done, night after night, hearkening to the deathwatches in the wall.

opened it—you cannot imagine how stealthily, stealthily—until, at length a single dim ray, like the thread of the spider, shot from out the crevice and fell full upon the vulture eye.

It was open—wide, wide open—and I grew furious as I gazed upon it. I saw it with perfect distinctness—all a dull blue, with a hideous veil over it that chilled the very marrow in my bones; but I could see nothing else of the old man's face or person; for I had directed the ray, as if by instinct, precisely upon the damned spot.

And have I not told you that what you mistake for madness is but over acuteness of the senses?—now, I say, there came to my ears a low, dull quick sound, such as a watch makes when enveloped in cotton. I knew that sound well, too. It was the beating of the old man's heart. It increased my fury, as the beating of a drum stimulates the soldier into courage.

But even yet I refrained and kept still. I scarcely breathed. I held the lantern motionless. I tried how steadily I could maintain the ray upon the eye. Meantime the hellish tattoo of the heart increased. It grew quicker and quicker, and louder and louder every instant. The old man's terror must have been extreme! It grew louder, I say, louder every moment!—do you mark me well? I have told you that I am nervous: so I am. And now at the dead hour of the night, amid the dreadful silence of that old house, so strange a noise as this excited me to uncontrollable terror. Yet, for some minutes longer I refrained and stood still. But the beating grew louder, louder! I thought the heart must burst. And now a new anxiety seized me—the sound would be heard by a neighbor! The old man's hour had come! With a loud yell, I threw open the lantern and leaped into the room. He shrieked once—only once. In an instant I dragged him to the floor, and pulled the

But even yet I refrained and kept still. I scarcely breathed. I held the lantern motionless.

A shriek had been heard by a neighbor during the night; suspicion of foul play had been aroused. . .

heavy bed over him. I then smiled gaily, to find the deed so far done. But, for many minutes, the heart beat on with a muffled sound. This, however, did not vex me; it would not be heard through the wall. At length it ceased. The old man was dead. I removed the bed and examined the corpse. Yes, he was stone, stone dead. I placed my hand upon the heart and held it there many minutes. There was no pulsation. He was stone dead. His eye would trouble me no more.

If still you think me mad, you will think so no longer when I describe the wise precautions I took for the concealment of the body. The night waned, and I worked hastily, but in silence. First of all I dismembered the corpse. I cut off the head and the arms and the legs.

I then took up three planks from the flooring of the chamber, and deposited all between the scantlings. I then replaced the boards so cleverly, so cunningly, that no human eye—not even his—could have detected anything wrong. There was nothing to wash out—no stain of any kind—no bloodspot whatever. I had been too wary for that. A tub had caught all—ha! ha!

When I had made an end of these labors, it was four o'clock—still dark as midnight. As the bell sounded the hour, there came a knocking at the street door. I went down to open it with a light heart,—for what had I now to fear? There entered three men, who introduced themselves, with perfect suavity, as officers of the police. A shriek had been heard by a neighbor during the night; suspicion of foul play had been aroused; information had been lodged at the police office, and they (the officers) had been deputed to search the premises.

I smiled,—for what had I to fear? I bade the gentlemen welcome. The shriek, I said, was my own in a dream. The old man, I mentioned, was absent in the country. I took my visitors all over the house. I bade them search—search well. I led them, at length, to his chamber. I showed them his treasures, secure, undisturbed. In the enthusiasm of my confidence, I brought chairs into the room, and desired them here to rest from their fatigues, while I myself, in the wild audacity of my perfect triumph, placed my own seat upon the very spot beneath which reposed the corpse of the victim.

The officers were satisfied. My manner had convinced them. I was singularly at ease. They sat, and while I answered cheerily, they chatted of familiar things. But, ere long, I felt myself getting pale and wished them gone. My head ached, and I fancied a ringing in my ears: but still they sat and still chatted. The ringing became more distinct:—it continued and became more distinct: I talked more freely to get rid of the feeling: but it continued and gained definiteness—until, at length, I found that the noise was not within my ears.

No doubt I now grew very pale;—but I talked more fluently, and with a heightened voice. Yet the sound increased—and what could I do? It was a low, dull, quick sound—such a sound as a watch makes when enveloped in cotton. I gasped for breath—and yet the officers heard it not. I talked more quickly—more vehemently; but the noise steadily increased. I arose and argued about trifles, in a high key and with violent gesticulations; but the noise steadily increased. Why would they not be gone? I paced the floor to and fro with heavy strides, as if excited to fury by the observations of the men—but the noise steadily increased. Oh God! what could I do? I foamed—I raved—I swore! I swung the chair upon which I had

The officers were satisfied. My manner had convinced them. I was singularly at ease.

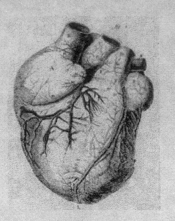

"Villains!" I shrieked, "Dissemble no more! I admit the deed!—tear up the planks! here, here!—it is the beating of his hideous heart!"

been sitting, and grated it upon the boards, but the noise rose over all and continually increased. It grew louder—louder—louder! And still the men chatted pleasantly, and smiled. Was it possible they heard not? Almighty God! no, no! They heard!—they suspected!—they knew!—they were making a mockery of my horror!—this I thought, and this I think. But anything was better than this agony! Anything was more tolerable than this derision! I could bear those hypocritical smiles no longer! I felt that I must scream or die! and now—again!—hark!—louder! louder! louder!

"Villains!" I shrieked, "Dissemble no more! I admit the deed!—tear up the planks! here, here!—it is the beating of his hideous heart!"

The Highwayman

by Alfred Noyes

Alfred Noyes

Alfred Noyes was born in 1880 in England. His father was a grocer and a teacher who taught him Latin and Greek at an early age. He attended college, but never finished— distinguishing himself instead on the rowing team. His first collection of poems was published when he was 21. He was for years Professor of Modern English Literature at Princeton University. He became blind in later years and had to dictate all his work. He died in 1958 and is buried in England.

The wind was a torrent of darkness among
    The gusty trees.
The moon was a ghostly galleon tossed upon cloudy seas.
The road was a ribbon of moonlight over the purple moor,
And the highwayman came riding—
    Riding—riding
The highwayman came riding, up to the old inn-door.

He'd a French cocked-hat on his forehead, a bunch
    Of lace at his chin,
A coat of the claret velvet, and breeches of brown doe-skin.
They fitted with never a wrinkle. His boots were
    Up to the thigh.
And he rode with a jewelled twinkle,
    His pistol butts a-twinkle,
His rapier hilt a-twinkle, under the jewelled sky.

Over the cobbles he clattered and clashed
    In the dark inn yard.
He tapped with his whip on the shutters, but all
    Was locked and barred.
He whistled a tune to the window, and who should be
    Waiting there
But the landlord's black-eyed daughter,
    Bess, the landlord's daughter,
Plaiting a dark red love-knot into her long black hair.

And dark in the dark old inn-yard a stable-wicket creaked
Where Tim the ostler listened. His face was white
    And peaked.
His eyes were hollows of madness, his hair like mouldy hay,
But he loved the landlord's daughter,
    The landlord's red-lipped daughter.
Dumb as a dog he listened, and he heard the robber say—
"One kiss, my bonny sweetheart, I'm after a prize tonight,
But I shall be back with the yellow gold before the
    Morning light;
Yet, if they press me sharply, and harry me through the day,
Then look for me by moonlight,
Watch for me by moonlight,
I'll come to thee by moonlight,
    Though hell should bar the way."

He rose upright in the stirrups. He scarce
    Could reach her hand,
But she loosened her hair in the casement.
    His face burnt like a brand
As the black cascade of perfume came
    Tumbling over his breast;
And he kissed its waves in the moonlight,
    (O, sweet black waves in the moonlight!)
Then he tugged at this rein in the moonlight, and galloped
    Away to the west.

He did not come in the dawning. He did not come at noon;
And out of the tawny sunset, before the rise of the moon,
When the road was a gypsy's ribbon, looping the
    Purple moor,
A red-coat troop came marching—
    Marching—marching—
King George's men came marching, up to the old inn-door.

*But I shall be back with the
yellow gold before the
Morning light. . .*

Look for me by moonlight;
Watch for my by
moonlight;
I'll come to thee by
moonlight, though hell
should bar the way!

They said no word to the landlord. They drank his
      Ale instead.
But they gagged his daughter, and bound her, to the foot of
      Her narrow bed.
Two of them knelt at her casement, with muskets
      At their side!
There was death at every window;
      And hell at one dark window;
For Bess could see, through her casement, the road
      That he would ride.

They had tied her up to attention, with many a
      Sniggering jest.
They had bound a musket beside her, with the muzzle
      Beneath her breast!
"Now, keep good watch!" and they kissed her.
She heard the doomed man say—
Look for me by moonlight;
      Watch for my by moonlight;
I'll come to thee by moonlight, though hell should bar the
way!

She twisted her hands behind her; but all the knots
      Held good!
She writhed her hands till her fingers were wet with sweat
      Or blood!
They stretched and strained in the darkness, and the hours
      Crawled by like years,
Till, now, on the stroke of midnight,
      Cold, on the stroke of midnight,
The tip of one finger touched it! The trigger at least was
hers!

The tip of one finger touched it. She strove no more
    For the rest.
Up, she stood up to attention, with the muzzle beneath
    Her breast.
She would not risk their hearing; she would not strive again;
For the road lay bare in the moonlight;
    Blank and bare in the moonlight;
And the blood of her veins, in the moonlight, throbbed
    To her love's refrain.

Tlot-tlot; tlot-tlot! Had they heard it? The horse-hoofs
    Ringing clear;
Tlot-tlot, tlot-tlot, in the distance? Were they deaf that they
    Did not hear?
Down the ribbon of moonlight, over the
    Brow of the hill,
The highwayman came riding—
    Riding—riding—
The red-coats looked to their
    Priming! She stood up, straight and still.

Tlot-tlot, in the frosty silence! Tlot-tlot, in the echoing night!
Nearer he came and nearer. Her face was like a light.
Her eyes grew wide for a moment; she drew one last
    Deep breath,
Then her finger moved in the moonlight,
    Her musket shattered the moonlight,
Shattered her breast in the moonlight and warned him—
    With her death.

He turned. He spurred to the west; he did not know
    Who stood
Bowed, with her head o'er the musket, drenched with her
    Own blood!
Not till the dawn he heard it, and his face grew grey to hear

Tlot-tlot; tlot-tlot! Had they heard it? The horse-hoofs Ringing clear; Tlot-tlot, tlot-tlot, in the distance? Were they deaf that they Did not hear?

The
Highwayman

A highwayman comes riding—
Riding—riding—
A highwayman comes riding, up to the old inn-door.

How Bess, the landlord's daughter,
        The landlord's black-eyed daughter,
Had watched for her love in the moonlight, and died
        In the darkness there.

Back he spurred like a madman, shouting a curse to the sky,
With the white road smoking behind him and his rapier
        Brandished high.
Blood-red were his spurs in the golden noon; wine-red
        Was his velvet coat;
When they shot him down on the highway,
        Down like a dog on the highway,
And he lay in his blood on the highway, with a bunch of lace
        At this throat.

And still of a winter's night, they say, when the wind
        Is in the trees,
When the moon is a ghostly galleon tossed upon cloudy seas,
When the road is a ribbon of moonlight over the purple
moor,
A highwayman comes riding—
        Riding—riding—
A highwayman comes riding, up to the old inn-door.

Over the cobbles he clatters and clangs in the dark inn-yard.
He taps with his whip on the shutters, but all is
        Locked and barred.
He whistles a tune to the window, and who should be
Waiting there
But the landlord's black-eyed daughter,
        Bess, the landlord's daughter,
Plaiting a dark red love-knot into her long black hair.

The Witches' Song

by William Shakespeare

*"Double, double toil and trouble;
Fire burn and cauldron bubble."*

Thrice the brinded cat hath mew'd.
Thrice, and once the hedge pig whin'd.
Harper cries, " 'Tis time, 'tis time."
Round about the cauldron go;
In the poison'd entrails throw.
Toad, that under cold stone
Days and nights has thirty-one
Swelter'd venom sleeping got,
Boil thou first i' the charmed pot.
  Double, double toil and trouble;
  Fire burn and cauldron bubble.

Fillet of a fenny snake,
In the cauldron boil and bake;
Eye of newt, and toe of frog,
Wool of bat, and tongue of dog,
Adder's fork, and blind-worm's sting,
Lizard's leg, and howler's wing,
For a charm of powerful trouble,
Like a hell-broth boil and bubble.
  Double, double toil and trouble;
  Fire burn and cauldron bubble.

Ticklers: Comic Tales

Essay

by Dr. Engel

When we travel by plane and check our luggage, it immediately becomes the dearest of Old Friends whom we long to see again at the end of our flight. Here is a woeful tale about a mortal injury suffered by one such friend.

Flying so frequently to my lecture sites, I'm always landing at airports where I know nobody in the town.

Flying so frequently to my lecture sites, I'm always landing at airports where I know nobody in the town. Be it Fargo or Fresno, as I exit the plane, I realize that the eager faces at the gate awaiting loved ones will look right past me to scan for that one special person. If I deplane early the faces that meet mine are happy and full of anticipation; if I'm one of the last, the faces look rather grim and anxious, fearing that their loved ones never made the flight.

Ironically, this very ritual is repeated by me a few minutes later at the level below in that high suspense area known as Baggage Claim. But now I'm the eager face in front of the conveyor belt anxiously scanning each piece of luggage as it moves into sight. Like those at the gate awaiting loved ones, I am at first all optimistic anticipation, hoping my familiar blue Hartmann suit bag will pop into view immediately, thus insuring a quick exit to my rental car. But when I've waited fifteen minutes and still not glimpsed my piece of luggage, my expression takes on the same fear and trepidation for my bag that those people at the gate had for their missing loved ones.

I've experienced lost luggage, late luggage, and lacerated luggage, but my most ghastly experience was in Dallas years ago. Waiting at the luggage carousel, I remember my initial disgusted reaction when the first bag to appear on the belt was none other than a large brown garbage bag, complete with loose yellow tie string and bulging sides. "Has it come to this?" I remember thinking, "that the quality of air passengers has sunk so low that some prefer Hefty to Louis Vuitton?" As the final degradation, I noticed as the bag passed by, two pairs of underwear could be seen protruding through a large rip in the plastic. I admit that from that moment I used one eye to spot my own bag and the other to see who in the world would claim the garbage bag.

By coincidence, nobody claimed the Hefty nor did my bag ever come into sight. Finally, I was the only one left at the carousel and the Hefty was the only thing circling. Not until then did I notice something appallingly familiar about the Fruit-of-the-Loom jockeys and something depressingly blue and Hartmannesque deep within the now slowly opening trash bag.

A revelation flashed upon me; somehow my bag must have been destroyed, and the handlers had tossed it and my orphaned belongings in their garbage bag of choice for me to claim. I was both furious and, idiotically, humiliated that my anonymous underpants had been on display for all of Flight #722 to snicker at in public.

Yes, the airline replaced the bag. I asked the agent how this could have happened, but she only shrugged and rolled her eyes.

Yes, the airline replaced the bag. I asked the agent how this could have happened, but she only shrugged and rolled her eyes. Visions of gorillas and Samsonites wrestling together danced through my mind.

I noticed that my exposed underwear had what looked like airplane grease on them. Rather than washing my dirty laundry in public, so to speak, I simply abandoned them in an airport trash container. As I wearily wandered to my rental car, I found myself humming a familiar tune. It was the Tony Bennett classic. He had left his heart in San Francisco; I had left my dirty drawers in Dallas.

The Adventures of Tom Sawyer
(Chapter Two)
by Mark Twain

Mark Twain

*Born **Samuel Clemens** in 1835, he later changed his name to Mark Twain, a term used on riverboats to measure the water depth. He studied for 2 years to be a riverboat captain on the Mississippi River, but never saw his dream come true—the time he graduated was the beginning of the Civil War and the Mississippi River was closed to riverboat traffic. His most famous book, **Huckleberry Finn**, received poor reviews when it was first released in 1885, but now Mark Twain is considered by many to be one of America's greatest writers and humorists.*

Ticklers: Comic Tales

Saturday morning was come, and all the summer world was bright and fresh, and brimming with life. There was a song in every heart; and if the heart was young the music issued at the lips. There was a cheer in every face and a spring in every step. The locust-trees were in bloom and the fragrance of the blossoms filled the air. Cardiff Hill, beyond the village and above it, was green with vegetation and it lay just far enough away to seem a Delectable Land, dreamy, reposeful, and inviting.

Tom appeared on the sidewalk with a bucket of whitewash and a long-handled brush. He surveyed the fence, and all gladness left him and a deep melancholy settled down upon his spirit. Thirty yards of board fence nine feet high. Life to him seemed hollow, and existence but a burden. Sighing, he dipped his brush and passed it along the topmost plank; repeated the operation; did it again; compared the insignificant whitewashed streak with the far-reaching continent of unwhitewashed fence, and sat down on a tree-box discouraged. Jim came skipping out at the gate with a tin pail, and singing Buffalo Gals. Bringing water from the town pump had always been hateful work in Tom's eyes, before, but now it did not strike him so. He remembered that there was company at the pump. White, mulatto, and negro boys and girls were always there waiting their turns, resting, trading playthings, quarrelling, fighting, skylarking. And he remembered that although the pump was only a hundred and fifty yards off, Jim never got back with a bucket of water under an hour—and even then somebody generally had to go after him. Tom said: 'Say, Jim, I'll fetch the water if you'll whitewash some.'

Jim shook his head and said: 'Can't, Mars Tom. Ole missis , she tole me I got to go an' git dis water an' not stop foolin' roun' wid anybody. She say she spec' Mars Tom gwine to ax me to whitewash, an' so she tole me go 'long an' 'tend to my own business—she 'lowed SHE'D 'tend to de whitewashin'.'

'Oh, never you mind what she said, Jim. That's the way she always talks. Gimme the bucket—I won't be gone only a minute. SHE won't ever know." 'Oh, I dasn't, Mars Tom. Ole missis she'd take an' tar de head off'n me. 'Deed she would.' "SHE! She never licks anybody—whacks 'em over the head with her thimble— and who cares for that, I'd like to know. She talks awful, but talk don't hurt—anyways it don't if she don't cry. Jim, I'll give you a marvel. I'll give you a white alley!"

Jim began to waver. "White alley, Jim! And it's a bully taw." "My! Dat's a mighty gay marvel, I tell you! But Mars Tom I's powerful 'fraid ole missis."

"And besides, if you will I'll show you my sore toe." Jim was only human—this attraction was too much for him. He put down his pail, took the white alley, and bent over the toe with absorbing interest while the bandage was being unwound. In another moment he was flying down the street with his pail and a tingling rear, Tom was whitewashing with vigor, and Aunt Polly was retiring from the field with a slipper in her hand and triumph in her eye.

But Tom's energy did not last. He began to think of

Tom said: "Say, Jim, I'll fetch the water if you'll whitewash some."

the fun he had planned for this day, and his sorrows multiplied. Soon the free boys would come tripping along on all sorts of delicious expeditions, and they would make a world of fun of him for having to work—the very thought of it burnt him like fire. He got out his worldly wealth and examined it—bits of toys, marbles, and trash; enough to buy an exchange of WORK, maybe, but not half enough to buy so much as half an hour of pure freedom. So he returned his straitened means to his pocket, and gave up the idea of trying to buy the boys. At this dark and hopeless moment an inspiration burst upon him! Nothing less than a great, magnificent inspiration.

He took up his brush and went tranquilly to work. Ben Rogers hove in sight presently; the very boy, of all boys, whole ridicule he had been dreading. Ben's gait was the hop-skip-and-jump proof enough that his heart was light and his anticipations high. He was eating an apple, and giving a long, melodious whoop, at intervals, followed by a deep toned ding-dong-dong, ding-dong-dong, for he was personating a steamboat. As he drew near, he slackened speed, took the middle of the street, leaned far over to starboard and rounded to ponderously and with laborious pomp and circumstance—for he was personating the Big Missouri, and considered himself to be drawing nine feet of water. He was boat and captain and engine bells combined, so he had to imagine himself standing on his own hurricane deck giving the orders and executing them: "Stop her, sir! Ting-a-ling-ling!" The headway ran almost out, and he drew up slowly toward the sidewalk. "Ship up to back! Ting-a-ling-ling!" His arms straightened and stiffened down his sides. "Set her back on the stabboard! Ting-a-ling-ling! Chow! ch-chow-wow! Chow!" His right hand, meantime, describing stately circles for it was representing a forty-foot wheel.

He was eating an apple, and giving a long, melodious whoop, at intervals, followed by a deep toned ding-dong-dong, ding-dong-dong, for he was personating a steamboat.

"Let her go back on the labboard! Ting-a-ling-ling! Chow-ch-chow-chow!" The left hand began to describe circles.

"Stop the stabboard! Ting-a-ling-ling! Stop the labboard! Come ahead on the stabboard! Stop her! Let your outside turn over slow! Ting-a-ling-ling! Chow-ow-ow! Get out that head-line! Lively now! Come out with your spring-line—what're you about there! Take a turn round that stump with the bight of it! Stand by that stage, now—let her go! Done with the engines, sir! Ting-a-ling-ling! Sh't! Sh't! Sh't!" (trying the gauge-cocks).

Tom went on whitewashing—paid no attention to the steamboat. Ben stared a moment and then said: "Hi-Yi! You're up a stump, ain't you!"

No answer. Tom surveyed his last touch with the eye of an artist, then he gave his brush another gentle sweep and surveyed the result, as before. Ben ranged up alongside of him. Tom's mouth watered for the apple, but he stuck to his work. Ben said: "Hello, old chap, you got to work, hey?"

Tom wheeled suddenly and said: "Why, it's you, Ben! I warn't noticing."

"Say, I'm going in a-swimming, I am. Don't you wish you could? But of course you' druther WORK, wouldn't you? Course you would!"

Tom contemplated the boy a bit, and said: "What do you call work?" "Why, ain't THAT work?"

Tom resumed his whitewashing, and answered carelessly: "Well, maybe it is, and maybe it ain't. All I know, is, it suits Tom Sawyer." "Oh come, now, you don't mean to let on that you LIKE it?" The brush continued to move. "Like it? Well, I don't see why I oughtn't to like it. Does a boy get a chance to whitewash a fence every day?"

That put the thing in a new light. Ben stopped

Tom surveyed his last touch with the eye of an artist, then he gave his brush another gentle sweep and surveyed the result, as before.

nibbling his apple. Tom swept his brush daintily back and forth—stepped back to note the effect—added a touch here and there, criticized the effect again, Ben watching every move and getting more and more interested, more and more absorbed. Presently he said: "Say, Tom, let ME whitewash a little."

Tom considered, was about to consent; but he altered his mind: "No, no, I reckon it wouldn't hardly do, Ben. You see, Aunt Polly's awful particular about this fence, right here on the street, you know, but if it was the back fence I wouldn't mind and SHE wouldn't. Yes, she's awful particular about this fence; it's got to be done very careful; I reckon there ain't one boy in a thousand, maybe two thousand, that can do it the way it's got to be done."

"No, is that so? Oh come, now, lemme just try. Only just a little, I'd let you, if you was me, Tom."

"Ben, I'd like to, honest injun; but Aunt Polly, well, Jim wanted to do it, but she wouldn't let him; Sid wanted to do it, and she wouldn't let Sid. Now don't you see how I'm fixed? If you was to tackle this fence and anything was to happen to it."

"Oh shucks, I'll be just as careful. Now lemme try. Say, I'll give you the core of my apple." "Well, here—no, Ben, now don't. I'm afeard." "I'll give you ALL of it!"

Tom gave up the brush with reluctance in his face, but alacrity in his heart. And while the late steamer Big Missouri worked and sweated in the sun, the retired artist sat on a barrel in the shade close by, dangled his legs, munched his apple, and planned the slaughter of more innocents. There was no lack of material; boys happened along every little while; they came to jeer, but remained to whitewash. By the time Ben was tuckered out, Tom had traded the next chance to Billy Fisher for a kite, in good repair; and when he played out, Johnny

"Oh shucks, I'll be just as careful. Now lemme try. Say, I'll give you the core of my apple." "Well, here—no, Ben, now don't. I'm afeard." "I'll give you ALL of it!"

Ticklers: Comic Tales

Miller bought in for a dead rat and a string to swing it with and so on, and so on, hour after hour. And when the middle of the afternoon came, from being a poor poverty-stricken boy in the morning, Tom was literally rolling in wealth. He had besides the things before mentioned, twelve marbles, part of a jews-harp, a piece of blue bottle glass to look through, a spool cannon, a key that wouldn't unlock anything, a fragment of chalk, a glass stopper of a decanter, a tin soldier, a couple of tadpoles, six fire crackers, a kitten with only one eye, a brass doorknob, a dog collar—but no dog, the handle of a knife, four pieces of orange peel, and a dilapidated old window sash.

He had had a nice, good, idle time all the while, plenty of company, and the fence had three coats of whitewash on it! If he hadn't run out of whitewash he would have bankrupted every boy in the village.

Tom said to himself that it was not such a hollow world, after all. He had discovered a great law of human action, without knowing it, namely, that in order to make a man or a boy covet a thing, it is only necessary to make the thing difficult to attain. If he had been a great and wise philosopher, like the writer of this book, he would now have comprehended that Work consists of whatever a body is obliged to do, and that Play consists of whatever a body is not obliged to do. And this would help him to understand why constructing artificial flowers or performing on a treadmill is work, while rolling ten pins or climbing Mont Blanc is only amusement. There are wealthy gentlemen in England who drive four-horse passenger coaches twenty or thirty miles on a daily line in the summer, because the privilege costs them considerable money; but if they were offered wages for the service, that would turn it into work and then they would resign.

He had besides the things before mentioned, twelve marbles, part of a jews-harp, a piece of blue bottle glass to look through, a spool cannon . . . six fire crackers, a kitten with only one eye. . .

Ticklers: Comic Tales

The Garden of Live Flowers

from

Through the Looking Glass

by Lewis Carroll

*The real Alice Liddell. Lewis Carroll protected her privacy when **Alice in Wonderland** was first published.*

"I should see the garden far better," said Alice to herself, "if I could get to the top of that hill: and here's a path that leads straight to it—at least, no, it doesn't do that—" (after going a few yards along the path, and turning several sharp corners), "but I suppose it will at last. But how curiously it twists! It's more like a corkscrew than a path! Well this turn goes to the hill, I suppose—no, it doesn't! This goes straight back to the house! Well then, I'll try it the other way."

And so she did: wandering up and down, and trying turn after turn, but always coming back to the house, do what she would. Indeed, once, when she turned a corner rather more quickly than usual, she ran against it before she could stop herself.

"It's no use talking about," Alice said, looking up at the house and pretending it was arguing with her. "I'm not going in again yet. I know I should have to get through the Looking-glass again—back into the old room—and there'd be an end of all my adventures!"

So, resolutely turning her back upon the house, she set out once more down the path, determined to keep straight on till she got to the hill. For a few minutes all went on well, and she was just saying "I really shall do it this time—" when the path gave a sudden twist and shook itself (as she described it afterwards), and the next moment she found herself actually walking in at the door.

"Oh, it's too bad!" she cried. "I never saw such a house for getting in the way! Never!"

However, there was a hill full in sight, so there was nothing to be done but start again. This time she came upon a large flowerbed, with a border of daisies, and a willow-tree growing in the middle.

"O Tiger-lily!" said Alice, addressing herself to one that was waving gracefully about in the wind, "I wish you could talk!"

"We can talk," said the Tiger-lily, "when there's anybody worth talking to."

Alice was so astonished that she couldn't speak for a minute: it quite seemed to take her breath away. At length, as the Tiger-lily only went on waving about, she spoke again, in a timid voice—almost in a whisper. "And can all the flowers talk?"

"As well as you can," said the Tiger-lily. "And a great deal louder."

"It isn't manners for us to begin, you know," said the Rose, "and I really was wondering when you'd speak! Said I to myself, 'Her face has got some sense in it, though it's not a clever one!' Still, you're the right colour, and that goes a long way."

"I don't care about the colour," the Tiger-lily remarked. "If only her petals curled up a little more, she'd be all right."

Alice didn't like being criticized, so she began asking questions. "Aren't you sometimes frightened at being planted out here, with nobody to take care of you?"

Lewis Carroll

Lewis Carroll was born Charles Lutwidge Dodgson in 1850 and had 10 brothers and sisters. He was a smart but very unusual child—he had a terrible stammer and was extremely shy and eccentric. At the age of 11, he attended Oxford University, where he stayed until he was 13, and never left. He was offered a teaching position which he held for the rest of his life. He was a great mathematician and loved photography. He met a young girl named Alice Liddell, and when she was 9, took her on a rowing trip. During this little adventure, he invented the entire story of **Alice in Wonderland** *in just 3½ hours.*

Ticklers: Comic Tales

"There's the tree in the middle," said the Rose. "What else is it good for?"

"But what could it do, if any danger came?" Alice asked.

"It could bark," said the Rose.

"It says 'Boughwough!'" cried a Daisy. "That's why its branches are called boughs!"

"Didn't you know that?" cried another Daisy. And here they all began shouting together, till the air seemed quite full of little shrill voices. "Silence, every one of you!" cried the Tiger-lily, waving itself passionately from side to side, and trembling with excitement. "They know I can't get at them!" it panted, bending its quivering head towards Alice, "or they wouldn't dare to do it!"

"Never mind!" Alice said in a soothing tone, and, stooping down to the daisies, who were just beginning again, she whispered "If you don't hold your tongues, I'll pick you!"

There was silence in a moment, and several of the pink daisies turned white.

"That's right!' said the Tiger-lily. "The daisies are worst of all. When one speaks, they all begin together, and it's enough to make one wither to hear the way they go on!"

"How is it you can all talk so nicely!" Alice said, hoping to get it into a better temper by a compliment. "I've been in many gardens before, but none of the flowers could talk."

"Put your hand down, and feel the ground," said the Tiger-lily. "Then you'll know why."

Alice did so. "It's very hard," she said; "but I don't see what that had to do with it."

"In most gardens," the Tiger-lily said, "they make the beds too soft – so that the flowers are always sleep."

"Never mind!" Alice said in a soothing tone, and, stooping down to the daisies, who were just beginning again, she whispered "If you don't hold your tongues, I'll pick you!"

This sounded a very good reason, and Alice was quite pleased to know it. "I never thought of that before!" she said.

"It's my opinion that you never think at all," the Rose said, in a rather severe tone.

"I never saw anybody that looked stupider," a Violet said, so suddenly, that Alice quite jumped; for it hadn't spoken before.

"Hold your tongue!" cried the Tiger-lily. "As if you ever saw anybody! You keep your head under the leaves, and snore away there, till you know no more what's going on in the world, than if you were a bud!'"

"Are there any more people in the garden besides me?" Alice said, not choosing to notice the Rose's last remark.

"There's one other flower in the garden that can move about like you," said the Rose. "I wonder how you do it—" ("You're always wondering," said the Tiger-lily), "but she's more bushy than you are."

"Is she like me?" Alice asked eagerly, for the thought crossed her mind, "There's another little girl in the garden, somewhere!"

"Well, she has the same awkward shape as you," the Rose said: "but she's redder—and her petals are shorter, I think."

"They're done up close, like a dahlia," said the Tiger-lily: "not tumbled about, like yours."

"But that's not your fault," the Rose added kindly. "You're beginning to fade, you know—and then one can't help one's petals getting a little untidy."

Alice didn't like this idea at all: so, to change the subject, she asked "Does she ever come out here?"

"I daresay you'll see her soon," said the Rose. "She's one of the kind that has nine spikes, you know."

"Where does she wear them?" Alice asked with

"Are there any more people in the garden besides me?" Alice said, not choosing to notice the Rose's last remark.

some curiosity.

"Why, all round her head, of course," the Rose replied. "I was wondering you hadn't got some too. I thought it was the regular rule."

"She's coming!" cried the Larkspur. "I hear her footstep, thump, thump, along the gravel-walk!"

Alice looked round eagerly and found that it was the Red Queen. "She's grown a good deal!" was her first remark. She had indeed: when Alice first found her in the ashes, she had been only three inches high— and here she was, half a head taller than Alice herself!

"It's the fresh air that does it," said the Rose: "wonderfully fine air it is, out here."

"I think I'll go and meet her," said Alice, for, though the flowers were interesting enough, she felt it would be far grander to have a talk with a real Queen.

"You can't possibly do that," said the Rose: "I should advise you to walk the other way."

This sounded nonsense to Alice, so she said nothing, but set off at once towards the Red Queen. To her surprise she lost sight of her in a moment, and found herself walking in at the front-door again.

A little provoked, she drew back, and, after looking everywhere for the Queen (whom she spied out at last, a long way off), she thought she would try the plan, this time, of walking in the opposite direction.

It succeeded beautifully. She had not been walking a minute before she found herself face to face with the Red Queen, and full in sight of the hill she had been so long aiming at.

"Where do you come from?" said the Red Queen. "And where are you going? Look up, speak nicely, and don't twiddle your fingers all the time."

Alice attended to all these directions, and explained, as well as she could, that she had lost her

Alice looked round eagerly and found that it was the Red Queen.

way.

"I don't know what you mean by your way," said the Queen: "all the ways about here belong to me—but why did you come out here at all?" she added in a kinder tone. "Curtsey while you're thinking what to say. It saves time."

Alice wondered a little at this, but she was too much in awe of the Queen to disbelieve it. "I'll try it when I go home," she thought to herself, "the next time I'm a little late for dinner."

"It's time for you to answer now," the Queen said looking at her watch: "open your mouth a little wider when you speak, and always say 'your Majesty.'"

"I only wanted to see what the garden was like, your Majesty—"

"That's right," said the Queen, patting her on the head, which Alice didn't like at all: "though, when you say 'garden' —I've seen gardens, compared with which this would be a wilderness."

Alice didn't dare to argue the point, but went on: "—and I thought I'd try and find my way to the top of that hill—"

"When you say 'hill'," the Queen interrupted, "I could show you hills, in comparison with which you'd call that a valley."

"No, I shouldn't," said Alice, surprised into contradicting her at last: "a hill can't be a valley, you know. That would be nonsense—"

The Red Queen shook her head. "You may call it 'nonsense' if you like," she said, "but I've heard nonsense, compared with which that would be as sensible as a dictionary!"

Alice curtseyed again, as she was afraid from the Queen's tone that she was a little offended: and they walked on in silence till they got to the top of the little

Alice didn't dare to argue the point, but went on: "—and I thought I'd try and find my way to the top of that hill—"

For some minutes Alice
stood without speaking,
looking out in all directions
over the country—and a
most curious country it
was.

Ticklers: Comic Tales

hill.

For some minutes Alice stood without speaking, looking out in all directions over the country—and a most curious country it was. There were a number of tiny little brooks running straight across it from side to side, and the ground between was divided up into squares by a number of little green hedges, that reached from brook to brook.

"I declare it's marked out just like a large chessboard!" Alice said at last. "There ought to be some men moving about somewhere—and so there are!" she added in a tone of delight, and her heart began to beat quickly with excitement as she went on. "It's a great huge game of chess that's being played—all over the world—if this is the world at all, you know. Oh, what fun it is! How I wish I was one of them! I wouldn't mind being a Pawn, if only I might join—though of course I should like to be a Queen, best."

She glanced rather shyly at the real Queen as she said this, but her companion only smiled pleasantly, and said "That's easily managed. You can be the White Queen's Pawn, if you like, as Lily's too young to play: and you're in the Second Square to begin with: when you get to the Eighth Square you'll be a Queen—" Just at this moment, somehow or other, they began to run.

Alice never could quite make out, in thinking it over afterwards, how it was that they began: all she remembers is, that they were running hand in hand, and the Queen went so fast that it was all she could do to keep up with her: and still the Queen kept crying "Faster! Faster!" but Alice felt she could not go faster, though she had no breath left to say so.

The most curious part of the thing was, that the trees and the other things round them never changed their places at all: however fast they went, they never seemed to pass anything. "I wonder if all the things move along with us?" thought poor puzzled Alice. And the Queen seemed to guess her thoughts, for she cried "Faster! Don't try to talk!"

Not that Alice had any idea of doing that. She felt as if she would never be able to talk again, she was getting so much out of breath: and still the Queen cried "Faster! Faster!" and dragged her along, "Are we nearly there?" Alice managed to pant out at last.

"Nearly there!" the Queen repeated. "Why, we passed it ten minutes ago! Faster!" And they ran on for a time in silence, with the wind whistling in Alice's ears, and almost blowing her hair off her head, she fancied.

"Now! Now!" cried the Queen. "Faster! Faster!" And they went so fast that at last they seemed to skim through the air, hardly touching the ground with their feet, till suddenly, just as Alice was getting quite exhausted, they stopped, and she found herself sitting on the ground, breathless and giddy.

The Queen propped her up against a tree, and said kindly, "You may rest a little, now."

Alice looked round her in great surprise, "Why, I do believe we've been under this tree the whole time! Everything's just as it was!"

"Of course it is," said the Queen. "What would you have it?"

"Well, in our country," said Alice, still panting a little, "you'd generally get to somewhere else—if you ran very fast for a long time as we've been doing."

"A slow sort of country!" said the Queen. "Now, here, you see, it takes all the running you can do, to keep in the same place. If you want to get somewhere else, you must run at least twice as fast as that!"

"I'd rather not try, please!" said Alice. "I'm quite

"Well, in our country," said Alice, still panting a little, "you'd generally get to somewhere else—if you ran very fast for a long time as we've been doing."

Alice did not know what to say to this, but luckily the Queen did not wait for an answer, but went on.

content to stay here—only I am so hot and thirsty!"

"I know what you'd like!" the Queen said good-naturedly, taking a little box out of her pocket. "Have a biscuit?"

Alice thought it would not be civil to say "No," though it wasn't at all what she wanted. She took it, and ate it as well as she could: and it was very dry: and she thought she had never been so nearly choked in all her life.

"While you're refreshing yourself," said the Queen, "I'll just take the measurements." And she took a ribbon out of her pocket, marked in inches, and began measuring the ground, and sticking little pegs in here and there.

"At the end of two yards," she said, putting in a peg to mark the distance, "I shall give you your directions—have another biscuit?"

"No, thank you," said Alice: "one's quite enough!"

"Thirst quenched, I hope?" said the Queen.

Alice did not know what to say to this, but luckily the Queen did not wait for an answer, but went on. "At the end of three yards I shall repeat them—for fear of your forgetting them. At the end of four, I shall say good-bye. And at the end of five, I shall go!"

She had got all the pegs put in by this time, and Alice looked on with great interest as she returned to the tree, and then began slowly walking down the row.

At the two-yard peg she faced round, and said "A pawn goes two squares in its first move, you know. So you'll go very quickly through the Third Square—by railway. I should think—and you'll find yourself in the Fourth Square in no time. Well, that square belongs to Tweedledum and Tweedledee—the Fifth is mostly water—the Sixth belongs to Humpty Dumpty—But you make no remark?"

"I—I didn't know I had to make one—just then," Alice faltered out.

"You should have said," the Queen went on in a tone of grave reproof, "It's extremely kind of you to tell me all this'—however, we'll suppose it said—the Seventh Square is all forest—however, one of the Knights will show you the way—and in the Eighth Square we shall be Queens together, and it's all feasting and fun!" Alice got up and curtseyed, and sat down again.

At the next peg the Queen turned again, and this time she said "Speak in French when you can't think of the English for a thing—turn out your toes as you walk—and remember who you are!" She did not wait for Alice to curtsey, this time, but walked on quickly to the next peg, where she turned for a moment to say "Good-bye," and then hurried on to the last.

How it happened, Alice never knew, but exactly as she came to the last peg, she was gone. Whether she vanished into the air, or whether she ran quickly into the wood ("and she can run very fast!" thought Alice), there was no way of guessing, but she was gone, and Alice began to remember that she was a Pawn, and that it would soon be time for her to move.

How it happened, Alice never knew, but exactly as she came to the last peg, she was gone.

James Thomas Fields

James Thomas Fields was born in 1817 in Portsmouth, New Hampshire. He started the first publishing house in Boston and sold printed books at the Old Corner Bookstore, which is still open today. Many famous literary giants were regular visitors to his bookstore—among them, Charles Dickens, Henry Wadsworth Longfellow, and William Thackeray. He wrote several volumes of poetry and introduced the royalty system so that authors could receive payment for their writings. It is said that he frequently played pool with Mark Twain.

Ticklers: Comic Tales

The Owl-Critic

by James Thomas Fields

"Who stuffed that white owl?" No one spoke in the shop,
The barber was busy, and he couldn't stop;
The customers, waiting their turns, were all reading
The "Daily," the "Herald," the "Post," little heeding
The young man who blurted out such a blunt question;
Not one raised a head, or even made a suggestion;
    And the barber kept on shaving.

"Don't you see, Mr. Brown,"
Cried the youth, with a frown,
"How wrong the whole thing is,
How preposterous each wing is,
How flattened the head is, how jammed down the neck
is—
In short, the whole owl, what an ignorant wreck 't is!
I make no apology;
I've learned owl-eology.
I've passed days and nights in a hundred collections,
And cannot be blinded to any deflections
Arising from unskillful fingers that fail
To stuff a bird right, from his beak to his tail.
Mister Brown! Mister Brown!
Do take that bird down,
Or you'll soon be the laughing stock all over town!"
    And the barber kept on shaving.

"I've studied owls,
And other night-fowls,
And I tell you
What I know to be true;

An owl cannot roost
With his limbs so unloosed;
No owl in this world
Ever had his claws curled,
Ever had his legs slanted,
Ever had his bill canted,
Ever had his neck screwed
Into that attitude.
He can't do it, because
"Tis against all bird-laws.
Anatomy teaches,
Ornithology preaches,
An owl has a toe
That can't turn out so!
I've made the white owl my study for years,
And to see such a job almost moves me to tears!
Mr. Brown, I'm amazed
You should be so gone crazed
As to put up a bird
In that posture absurd!
To look at that owl really brings on a dizziness.
The man who stuffed him don't half know his business!"
    And the barber kept on shaving.

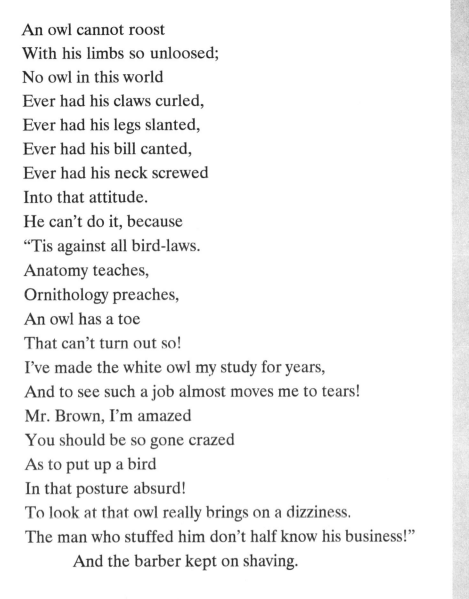

"Examine those eyes.
I'm filled with surprise
Taxidermists should pass
Off on you such poor glass;
So unnatural they seem
They'd make Audubon scream,
And John Burroughs laugh
To encounter such chaff.
Do take that bird down;
Have him stuffed again, Brown!"
    And the barber kept on shaving.

"With some sawdust and bark
I could stuff in the dark
An owl better than that.
I could make an old hat
Look more like an owl
Than that horrid fowl,
Stuck up there so stiff like a side of coarse leather.
In fact, about him there's not one natural feather."

Just then, with a wink and a sly normal lurch,
The owl, very gravely, got down from his perch,
Walked around, and regarded his fault-finding critic
(Who thought he was stuffed) with a glance analytic,
And then fairly hooted, as if he should say:
"Your learning's at fault this time, anyway;
Don't waste it again on a live bird, I pray.
I'm an owl; you're another. Sir Critic, good day!"
        And the barber kept on shaving.

The Goops

by Gelett Burgess

The Goops they lick their fingers,
And the Goops they lick their knives;
They spill their broth on the tablecloth—
Oh, they lead disgusting lives!
The Goops they talk while eating,
And loud and fast they chew;
And that is why I'm glad that I
Am not a Goop—are you?

Gelett Burgess

Gelett Burgess was born in Boston in 1866 and was known as a poet and cartoonist (the picture above is a cartoon of himself). He was mischievous as a child and is said to have carved his initials into the top of every church steeple in Boston. He is credited with inventing the word "blurb," which we still use today to describe short, descriptive phrases that are used to entice people to want to find out more about a subject. He served as an instructor at the University of California at Berkeley until he was fired for knocking down a statue he considered to be an eyesore. He later founded the San Francisco Boys Club, the first of its kind in America.

Ticklers: Comic Tales

Animal Antics

The Animal involved in this particular essay is a bear from the Shakespearean period. It was introduced to me by a most peculiar Old Friend—an anonymous young English teacher.

Oddly, it concerns a chained bear, a student teacher, and my high school's longest losing streak.

Essay

by Dr. Engel

I have been told on many occasions by those who listen to my lectures in person or on tape that they remember the trivia I mention in passing more vividly than some of the major themes of my talks. Such comments I consider as compliments since I admit to spending at least as much time gathering the supporting trifles as I do on my most important biographical or analytic points. I always felt that an ultimate triumph would be if I could pass on some trivia concerning the word trivia itself. And, voila, here it is: though the word is the plural form of the Latin word trivium, there has never been that singular form in English. How's that for a singular piece on plural trivia?

Just last week at a talk I gave at a teacher's meeting in Miami, I was asked how long I've been dredging up trivia for my talks. The question brought to mind the genesis of my devotion to the memorable minor detail. Oddly, it concerns a chained bear, a student teacher, and my high school's longest losing streak.

The year was 1964, and I was a sophomore in high school. Though I had had my share of inspiring and inspired English teachers, I suffered a real setback when I was assigned to old Mrs. McMuttersome's class. As you can surmise, I am using a Dickensian name rather than her real one. I would not want to offend her if she is still alive, though with her apparent age of ninety-six back then, the odds seem distinctly against it.

In any case, she was thirty years beyond her best

teaching period and started each class by muttering the ominous question: "Who can tell me what we were discussing last time?" We soon discovered that she was just like the rest of us in not having the vaguest idea as to the correct answer. The fifty-two minutes we spent in her class five times a week became my personal translation of ad infinitum.

But then, halfway through the semester we were saved by a student teacher assigned to our class. Mrs. McMuttersome took full advantage of her helper and vanished into the smoke-filled faculty lounge for the duration of the young woman's stay. I don't remember her name, but I'll never forget her teaching style: completely captivating. She was either born in a cradle of chalk-dust or was a female descendant of Mr. Chips. She was everything Mrs. M was not—enthusiastic, involved, prepared, and articulate.

Her passion was Shakespeare, and it soon became mine. Her one lecture that I'll never forget was given on a Monday morning following our basketball team's greatest victory over our archrival. We had gone 0 & 13 for the season; they were city champions and heavily favored. But we beat them by two points in the final two seconds. The underdog had won, and there was great excitement as we filed into her class first period the following Monday.

As I took my seat, I glanced at the blackboard and noticed a drawing of a large bear chained to a post. Her lecture was on Shakespeare's Globe Theater; I was disappointed that she launched into it without saying a word about the remarkable victory on Saturday. Instead, she began by emphasizing how great Shakespeare's dramatic skills had to be to compete with the other games and entertainment occurring simultaneously and in the same small arena of the theater.

Her passion was Shakespeare, and it soon became mine.

Animal Antics

For what other author so devoted himself to the cause of the downtrodden, from poor mistreated little Oliver, Smike, and Pip to the ultimate romantic underdoggery of Sidney Carton?

She walked to the blackboard, pointed to the animal, and asked if we had ever heard of "bear-baiting." We hadn't. It was Shakespeare's noisiest competition. As sport, they would release dogs to attack the captive bear, with men betting on the winner. Certain dogs were trained to jump at the bear's throat; others ran under its legs trying to bring it down with bites to the haunches. Those leaping at the throat were called "top-dogs"; those running beneath the bear had the longest odds of success and were called, of course, "underdogs"—"just as our basketball team had been!" she exclaimed with a smile.

I was enchanted both by the piece of trivia and by its simple connection to our basketball victory. And I'm wondering if perhaps this anonymous student teacher might have led me to my specialization in Charles Dickens. For what other author so devoted himself to the cause of the downtrodden, from poor mistreated little Oliver, Smike, and Pip to the ultimate romantic underdoggery of Sidney Carton? Moreover, by relating the delightful tidbit of the bear baiting, she showed me how to set a student's imagination on fire, and she fired the starting gun for my own lifelong academic race of trivial pursuit.

Robert Frost

The poet Robert Frost was born in San Francisco in 1874. His full name was Robert E. Lee Frost, named for the famous southern Civil War general. Both his mother and father were school teachers, and because his mother hated to cook or clean, they always lived in hotels. He moved to New Hampshire when he was 11 and fell in love with the cold weather and snow of New England. He was never a good student but loved baseball. Frost won four Pulitizer Prizes during his lifetime and lived to be 88 years old. He is buried in Vermont.

The Pasture

by Robert Frost

I'm going out to clean the pasture spring;
I'll only stop to rake the leaves away
(And wait to watch the water clear, I may):
I sha'n't be gone long.—You come too.

I'm going out to fetch the little calf
That's standing by the mother. It's so young,
It totters when she licks it with her tongue.
I sha'n't be gone long.—You come too.

From

From The Jungle Book

by Rudyard Kipling

This is the story of the great war that Rikki-tikki-tavi fought single-handed, through the bathrooms of the big bungalow in Segowlee cantonment. Darzee the Tailorbird helped him, and Chuchundra the Muskrat, who never comes out into the middle of the floor, but always creeps round by the wall, gave him advice, but Rikki-tikki did the real fighting. He was a mongoose, rather like a little cat in his fur and his tail, but quite like a weasel in his head and his habits. His eyes and the end of his restless nose were pink. He could scratch himself anywhere he pleased with any leg, front or back that he chose to use. He could fluff up his tail till it looked like a bottle brush, and his war cry as he scuttled through the long grass was: Rikk-tikk-tikki-tikki-tchk!

One day, a high summer flood washed him out of the burrow where he lived with his father and mother, and carried him, kicking and clucking, down a roadside ditch. He found a little wisp of grass floating there, and clung to it till he lost his senses. When he revived, he was lying in the hot sun on the middle of a garden path, very draggled indeed, and a small boy was saying, "Here's a dead mongoose. Let's have a funeral."

"No," said his mother, "let's take him in and dry him. Perhaps he isn't really dead."

They took him into the house, and a big man picked

Rudyard Kipling

Rudyard Kipling was born in Bombay, India, in 1865. His early years were spent in India—a happy time full of exotic sights and sounds. At age 5, he was very sad when he was sent back to England to live with a foster family. Poor eyesight handicapped him from participating in sports, and he spent all of his time on his literary abilities. At age 16, many of his remarkable poems and stories were published by the newspaper where he was working as a reporter. He lived for a while in Vermont, but returned to England where he was offered many honors by King George V. He humbly declined but later won the Nobel Prize for Literature in 1907.

"Now," said the big man (he was an Englishman who had just moved into the bungalow), "don't frighten him, and we'll see what he'll do."

him up between his finger and thumb and said he was not dead but half choked. So they wrapped him in cotton wool, and warmed him over a little fire, and he opened his eyes and sneezed.

"Now," said the big man (he was an Englishman who had just moved into the bungalow), "don't frighten him, and we'll see what he'll do."

It is the hardest thing in the world to frighten a mongoose, because he is eaten up from nose to tail with curiosity. The motto of all the mongoose family is "Run and find out," and Rikki-tikki was a true mongoose. He looked at the cotton wool, decided that it was not good to eat, ran all round the table, sat up and put his fur in order, scratched himself, and jumped on the small boy's shoulder.

"Don't be frightened, Teddy," said his father. "That's his way of making friends."

"Ouch! He's tickling under my chin," said Teddy.

Rikki-tikki looked down between the boy's collar and neck, snuffed at his ear, and climbed down to the floor, where he sat rubbing his nose.

"Good gracious," said Teddy's mother, "and that's a wild creature! I suppose he's so tame because we've been so kind to him."

"All mongooses are like that," said her husband. "If Teddy doesn't pick him up by the tail, or try to put him in a cage, he'll run in and out of the house all day long. Let's give him something to eat."

They gave him a little piece of raw meat. Rikki-tikki liked it immensely, and when it was finished he went out into the veranda and sat in the sunshine and fluffed up his fur to make it dry to the roots. Then he felt better.

"There are more things to find out about in this house," he said to himself, "than all my family could find out in all their lives. I shall certainly stay and find out."

He spent all day roaming over the house. He nearly drowned himself in the bathtubs, put his nose into the ink on a writing table, and burned it on the end of the big man's cigar, for he climbed up in the big man's lap to see how writing was done. At nightfall he ran into Teddy's nursery to watch how kerosene lamps were lighted, and when Teddy went to bed Rikki-tikki climbed up too. But he was a restless companion, because he had to get up and attend to every noise all through the night, and find out what made it. Teddy's mother and father came in, the last thing, to look at their boy, and Rikki-tikki was awake on the pillow. "I don't like that," said Teddy's mother. "He may bite the child." "He'll do no such thing," said the father. "Teddy's safer with that little beast than if he had a bloodhound to watch him. If a snake came into the nursery now—"

But Teddy's mother wouldn't think of anything so awful.

Early in the morning Rikki-tikki came to early breakfast in the veranda riding on Teddy's shoulder, and they gave him banana and some boiled egg. He sat on all their laps one after the other, because every well-brought-up mongoose always hopes to be a house mongoose some day and have rooms to run about in; and Rikki-tikki's mother (she used to live in the general's house at Segowlee) had carefully told Rikki what to do if ever he came across white men.

Then Rikki-tikki went out into the garden to see what was to be seen. It was a large garden, only half cultivated, with bushes, as big as summerhouses, of Marshall Niel roses, lime and orange trees, clumps of bamboos, and thickets of high grass. Rikki-tikki licked

It was a large garden, only half cultivated, with bushes, as big as summerhouses. . .

his lips. "This is a splendid hunting ground," he said, and his tail grew bottle-brushy at the thought of it, and he scuttled up and down the garden, snuffing here and there till he heard very sorrowful voices in a thornbush. It was Darzee the Tailorbird and his wife. They had made a beautiful nest by pulling two big leaves together and stitching them up the edges with fibers, and had filled the hollow with cotton and downy fluff. The nest swayed to and fro, as they sat on the rim and cried.

"What is the matter?" asked Rikki-tikki.

"We are very miserable," said Darzee. "One of our babies fell out of the nest yesterday and Nag ate him."

"H'm!" said Rikki-tikki, "that is very sad—but I am a stranger here. Who is Nag?"

Darzee and his wife only cowered down in the nest without answering, for from the thick grass at the foot of the bush there came a low hiss—a horrid cold sound that made Rikki-tikki jump back two clear feet. Then inch by inch out of the grass rose up the head and spread hood of Nag, the big black cobra, and he was five feet long from tongue to tail. When he had lifted one-third of himself clear of the ground, he stayed balancing to and fro exactly as a dandelion tuft balances in the wind, and he looked at Rikki-tikki with the wicked snake's eyes that never change their expression, whatever the snake may be thinking of.

"Who is Nag?" said he. "I am Nag. The great God Brahm put his mark upon all our people, when the first cobra spread his hood to keep the sun off Brahm as he slept. Look, and be afraid!"

He spread out his hood more than ever, and Rikki-tikki saw the spectacle mark on the back of it that looks exactly like the eye part of a hook-and-eye fastening. He was afraid for the minute, but it is impossible for a mongoose to stay frightened for any length of time, and

"We are very miserable," said Darzee. "One of our babies fell out of the nest yesterday and Nag ate him."

though Rikki-tikki had never met a live cobra before, his mother had fed him on dead ones, and he knew that all a grown mongoose's business in life was to fight and eat snakes. Nag knew that too and, at the bottom of his cold heart, he was afraid.

"Well," said Rikki-tikki, and his tail began to fluff up again, "marks or no marks, do you think it is right for you to eat fledglings out of a nest?"

Nag was thinking to himself, and watching the least little movement in the grass behind Rikki-tikki. He knew that mongooses in the garden meant death sooner or later for him and his family, but he wanted to get Rikki-tikki off his guard. So he dropped his head a little, and put it on one side.

"Let us talk," he said. "You eat eggs. Why should not I eat birds?"

"Behind you! Look behind you!" sang Darzee.

Rikki-tikki knew better than to waste time in staring. He jumped up in the air as high as he could go, and just under him whizzed by the head of Nagaina, Nag's wicked wife. She had crept up behind him as he was talking, to make an end of him. He heard her savage hiss as the stroke missed. He came down almost across her back, and if he had been an old mongoose he would have known that then was the time to break her back with one bite; but he was afraid of the terrible lashing return stroke of the cobra. He bit, indeed, but did not bite long enough, and he jumped clear of the whisking tail, leaving Nagaina torn and angry.

"Wicked, wicked Darzee!" said Nag, lashing up as high as he could reach toward the nest in the thornbush. But Darzee had built it out of reach of snakes, and it only swayed to and fro.

Rikki-tikki felt his eyes growing red and hot (when a mongoose's eyes grow red, he is angry), and he sat back

"Well," said Rikki-tikki, and his tail began to fluff up again, "marks or no marks, do you think it is right for you to eat fledglings out of a nest?"

on his tail and hind legs like a little kangaroo, and looked all around him, and chattered with rage. But Nag and Nagaina had disappeared into the grass. When a snake misses its stroke, it never says anything or gives any sign of what it means to do next. Rikki-tikki did not care to follow them, for he did not feel sure that he could manage two snakes at once. So he trotted off to the gravel path near the house, and sat down to think. It was a serious matter for him.

If you read the old books of natural history, you will find they say that when the mongoose fights the snake and happens to get bitten, he runs off and eats some herb that cures him. That is not true. The victory is only a matter of quickness of eye and quickness of foot— snake's blow against mongoose's jump—and as no eye can follow the motion of a snake's head when it strikes, this makes things much more wonderful than any magic herb. Rikki-tikki knew he was a young mongoose, and it made him all the more pleased to think that he had managed to escape a blow from behind.

It gave him confidence in himself, and when Teddy came running down the path, Rikki-tikki was ready to be petted.

It gave him confidence in himself, and when Teddy came running down the path, Rikki-tikki was ready to be petted. But just as Teddy was stooping, something wriggled a little in the dust, and a tiny voice said, "Be careful. I am Death!" It was Karait, the dusty brown snakeling that lies for choice on the dusty earth; and his bite is as dangerous as the cobra's. But he is so small that nobody thinks of him, and so he does the more harm to people.

Rikki-tikki's eyes grew red again, and he danced up to Karait with the peculiar rocking, swaying motion that he had inherited from his family. It looks very funny, but it is so perfectly balanced a gait that you can fly off from it at any angle you please, and in dealing with snakes this is an advantage.

If Rikki-tikki had only known, he was doing a much more dangerous thing than fighting Nag, for Karait is so small, and can turn so quickly, that unless Rikki bit him close to the back of the head, he would get the return stroke in his eye or lip. But Rikki did not know. His eyes were all red, and he rocked back and forth, looking for a good place to hold. Karait struck out. Rikki jumped sideways and tried to run in, but the wicked little dusty gray head lashed within a fraction of his shoulder, and he had to jump over the body, and the head followed his heels close.

Teddy shouted to the house: "Oh, look here!" Our mongoose is killing a snake." And Rikki-tikki heard a scream from Teddy's mother. His father ran out with a stick, but by the time he came up, Karait had lunged out once too far, and Rikki-tikki had sprung, jumped on the snake's back, dropped his head far between his forelegs, bitten as high up the back as he could get hold, and rolled away.

That bite paralyzed Karait, and Rikki-tikki was just going to eat him up from the tail, after the custom of his family at dinner, when he remembered that a full meal makes a slow mongoose, and if he wanted all his strength and quickness ready, he must keep himself thin. He went away for a dust bath under the castor-oil bushes, while Teddy's father beat the dead Karait.

"What is the use of that?" thought Rikki-tikki. "I have settled it all."

And then Teddy's mother picked him up from the dust and hugged him, crying that he had saved Teddy from death, and Teddy's father said that he was providence, and Teddy looked on with big scared eyes. Rikki-tikki was rather amused at all the fuss, which, of course, he did not understand. Teddy's mother might just as well have petted Teddy for playing in the dust.

If Rikki-tikki had only known, he was doing a much more dangerous thing than fighting Nag, for Karait is so small, and can turn so quickly, that unless Rikki bit him close to the back of the head, he would get the return stroke in his eye or lip.

Animal Antics

Chuchundra is a broken-hearted little beast. He whimpers and cheeps all the night, trying to make up his mind to run into the middle of the room. But he never gets there.

Rikki was thoroughly enjoying himself.

That night at dinner, walking to and fro among the wineglasses on the table, he might have stuffed himself three times over with nice things. But he remembered Nag and Nagaina, and though it was very pleasant to be patted and petted by Teddy's mother, and to sit on Teddy's shoulder, his eyes would get red from time to time, and he would go off into his long war cry of "Rikk-tikk-tikki-tikki-tchk!"

Teddy carried him off to bed, and insisted on Rikki-tikki sleeping under his chin. Rikki-tikki was too well bred to bite or scratch, but as soon as Teddy was asleep he went off for his nightly walk round the house, and in the dark he ran up against Chuchundra the Muskrat creeping around the wall. Chuchundra is a broken-hearted little beast. He whimpers and cheeps all the night, trying to make up his mind to run into the middle of the room. But he never gets there.

"Don't kill me," said Chuchundra, almost weeping. "Rikki-tikki, don't kill me!"

"Do you think a snake-killer kills muskrats!" said Rikki-tikki scornfully.

"Those who kill snakes get killed by snakes," said Chuchundra, more sorrowfully than ever. "And how am I to be sure that Nag won't mistake me for you some dark night?"

"There's not the least danger," said Rikki-tikki. "But Nag is in the garden, and I know you don't go there."

"My cousin Chua the Rat told me—" said Chuchundra, and then he stopped.

"Told you what?"

"H'sh! Nag is everywhere, Rikki-tikki. You should have talked to Chua in the garden."

"I didn't—so you must tell me. Quick, Chuchundra,

or I'll bite you!"

Chuchundra sat down and cried till the tears rolled off his whiskers. "I am a very poor man," he sobbed. "I never had spirit enough to run out into the middle of the room. H'sh! I mustn't tell you anything. Can't you hear, Rikki-tikki?"

Rikki-tikki listened. The house was as still as still, but he thought he could just catch the faintest scratch-scratch in the world—a noise as faint as that of a wasp walking on a windowpane—the dry scratch of a snake's scales on brickwork.

"That's Nag or Nagaina," he said to himself, "and he is crawling into the bathroom sluice. You're right Chuchundra; I should have talked to Chua."

He stole off to Teddy's bathroom, but there was nothing there, and then to Teddy's mother's bathroom. At the bottom of the smooth plaster wall there was a brick pulled out to make a sluice for the bath water, and as Rikki-tikki stole in by the masonry curb where the bath is put, he heard Nag and Nagaina whispering together outside in the moonlight.

"When the house is emptied of people," said Nagaina to her husband, "he will have to go away, and then the garden will be our own again."

"When the house is emptied of people," said Nagaina to her husband, "he will have to go away, and then the garden will be our own again. Go in quietly, and remember that the big man who killed Karait is the first one to bite. Then come out and tell me, and we will hunt for Rikki-tikki together."

"But are you sure that there is anything to be gained by killing the people?" said Nag.

"Everything. When there were no people in the bungalow, did we have any mongoose in the garden? So long as the bungalow is empty, we are king and queen of the garden; and remember that as soon as our eggs in the melon bed hatch (as they may tomorrow), our children will need room and quiet."

Animal Antics

Angry as he was, Rikki-tikki was very frightened as he saw the size of the big cobra.

"I had not thought of that," said Nag. "I will go, but there is no need that we should hunt for Rikki-tikki afterward. I will kill the big man and his wife, and the child if I can, and come away quietly. Then the bungalow will be empty, and Rikki-tikki will go."

Rikki-tikki tingled all over with rage and hatred at this, and then Nag's head came through the sluice, and his five feet of cold body followed it. Angry as he was, Rikki-tikki was very frightened as he saw the size of the big cobra. Nag coiled himself up, raised his head, and looked into the bathroom in the dark, and Rikki could see his eyes glitter.

"Now, if I kill him here, Nagaina will know; and if I fight him on the open floor, the odds are in his favor. What am I to do?" said Rikki-tikki-tavi.

Nag waved to and fro, and then Rikki-tikki heard him drinking from the biggest water jar that was used to fill the bath. "That is good," said the snake. "Now, when Karait was killed, the big man had a stick. He may have that stick still, but when he comes in to bathe in the morning he will not have a stick. I shall wait here till he comes. Nagaina—do you hear me?—I shall wait here in the cool till daytime."

There was no answer from outside, so Rikki-tikki knew Nagaina had gone away. Nag coiled himself down, coil by coil, round the bulge at the bottom of the water jar, and Rikki-tikki stayed still as death. After an hour he began to move, muscle by muscle, toward the jar. Nag was asleep, and Rikki-tikki looked at his big back, wondering which would be the best place for a good hold. "If I don't break his back at the first jump," said Rikki, "he can still fight. And if he fights—O Rikki!" He looked at the thickness of the neck below the hood, but that was too much for him; and a bite near the tail would only make Nag savage.

"It must be the head," he said at last; "the head above the hood. And, when I am once there, I must not let go."

Then he jumped. The head was lying a little clear of the water jar, under the curve of it; and, as his teeth met, Rikki braced his back against the bulge of the red earthenware to hold down the head. This gave him just one second's purchase, and he made the most of it. Then he was battered to and fro as a rat is shaken by a dog—to and fro on the floor, up and down, and around in great circles, but his eyes were red and he held on as the body cart-whipped over the floor, upsetting the tin dipper and the soap dish and the flesh brush, and banged against the tin side of the bath.

As he held he closed his jaws tighter and tighter, for he made sure he would be banged to death, and, for the honor of his family, he preferred to be found with his teeth locked. He was dizzy, aching, and felt shaken to pieces when something went off like a thunderclap just behind him. A hot wind knocked him senseless and red fire singed his fur. The big man had been wakened by the noise, and had fired both barrels of a shotgun into Nag just behind the hood.

Rikki-tikki held on with his eyes shut, for now he was quite sure he was dead. But the head did not move, and the big man picked him up and said, "It's the mongoose again, Alice. The little chap has saved our lives now."

Then Teddy's mother came in with a very white face, and saw what was left of Nag, and Rikki-tikki dragged himself to Teddy's bedroom and spent half the rest of the night shaking himself tenderly to find out whether he really was broken into forty pieces, as he fancied.

When morning came he was very stiff, but well

"It must be the head," he said at last; "the head above the hood. And, when I am once there, I must not let go."

"Nag is dead—is dead—is dead!" sang Darzee.

pleased with his doings. "Now I have Nagaina to settle with, and she will be worse than five Nags, and there's no knowing when the eggs she spoke of will hatch. Goodness! I must go see Darzee," he said.

Without waiting for breakfast, Rikki-tikki ran to the thornbush where Darzee was singing a song of triumph at the top of his voice. The news of Nag's death was all over the garden, for the sweeper had thrown the body on the rubbish heap.

"Oh, you stupid tuft of feathers!" said Rikki-tikki angrily. "Is this the time to sing!"

"Nag is dead—is dead—is dead!" sang Darzee. "The valiant Rikki-tikki caught him by the head and held fast. The big man brought the bang stick, and Nag fell in two pieces! He will never eat my babies again."

"All that's true enough. But where's Nagaina?" said Rikki-tikki, looking carefully round him.

"Nagaina came to the bathroom sluice and called for Nag," Darzee went on, "and Nag came out on the end of a stick—the sweeper picked him up on the end of stick and threw him upon the rubbish heap. Let us sing about the great, the red-eyed Rikki-tikki!" And Darzee filled his throat and sang.

"If I could get up to your nest, I'd roll your babies out!" said Rikki-tikki. "You don't know when to do the right thing at the right time. You're safe enough in your nest there, but it's war for me down here. Stop singing a minute, Darzee."

"For the great, the beautiful Rikki-tikki's sake I will stop," said Darzee. "What is it, O Killer of the terrible Nag?"

Where is Nagaina, for the third time?"

"On the rubbish heap by the stables, mourning for Nag. Great is Rikki-tikki with the white teeth."

"Bother my white teeth! Have you ever heard where

she keeps her eggs?"

"In the melon bed, on the end nearest the wall, where the sun strikes nearly all day. She hid them there weeks ago."

"And you never thought it worth while to tell me? The end nearest the wall, you said?"

"Rikki-tikki, you are not going to eat her eggs?"

"Not eat exactly, no. Darzee, if you have a grain of sense you will fly off to the stables and pretend that your wing is broken, and let Nagaina chase you away to this bush. I must get to the melon bed, and if I went there now she'd see me."

Darzee was a feather-brained little fellow who could never hold more than one idea at a time in his head. And just because he knew that Nagaina's children were born in eggs like his own, he didn't think at first that it was fair to kill them. But his wife was a sensible bird, and she knew that cobra's eggs meant young cobras later on. So she flew off from the nest, and left Darzee to keep the babies warm, and continue his song about the death of Nag. Darzee was very like a man some ways.

She fluttered in front of Nagaina by the rubbish heap and cried out, "Oh, my wing is broken! The boy in the house threw a stone at me and broke it." Then she fluttered more desperately than ever.

Nagaina lifted up her head and hissed, "You warned Rikki-tikki when I would have killed him. Indeed and truly, you've chosen a bad place to be lame in." And she moved toward Darzee's wife, slipping along over the dust.

"The boy broke it with a stone!" shrieked Darzee's wife.

"Well! It may be some consolation to you when you're dead to know that I shall settle accounts with the

Darzee was a feather-brained little fellow who could never hold more than one idea at a time in his head. And just because he knew that Nagaina's children were born in eggs like his own, he didn't think at first that it was fair to kill them.

Darzee's wife knew better than to do that, for a bird who looks at a snake's eyes gets so frightened that she cannot move.

boy. My husband lies on the rubbish heap this morning, but before night the boy in the house will lie very still. What is the use of running away? I am sure to catch you. Little fool, look at me!"

Darzee's wife knew better than to do that, for a bird who looks at a snake's eyes gets so frightened that she cannot move. Darzee's wife fluttered on, piping sorrowfully, and never leaving the ground, and Nagaina quickened her pace.

Rikki-tikki heard them going up the path from the stables, and he raced for the end of the melon patch near the wall. There, in the warm litter above the melons, very cunningly hidden, he found twenty-five eggs, about the size of bantam's eggs, but with whitish skins instead of shells.

"I was not a day too soon," he said, for he could see the baby cobras curled up inside the skin, and he knew that the minute they hatched they could each kill a man or a mongoose. He bit off the tops of the eggs as fast as he could, taking care to crush the young cobras, and turned over the litter from time to time to see whether he had missed any. At last there were only three eggs left, and Rikki-tikki began to chuckle to himself, when he heard Darzee's wife screaming:

"Rikki-tikki, I lead Nagaina toward the house, and she had gone into the veranda, and—oh, come quickly—she means killing!"

Rikki-tikki smashed two eggs, and tumbled backward down the melon bed with the third egg in his mouth, and scuttled to the veranda as hard as he could put foot to the ground. Teddy and his mother and father were there at early breakfast, but Rikki-tikki saw that they were not eating anything. They sat stone-still, and their faces were white. Nagaina was coiled up on the matting by Teddy's chair, within easy striking distance of Teddy's bare leg, and she was swaying to and fro, singing a song of triumph.

"Son of the big man that killed Nag," she hissed, "stay still. I am not ready yet. Wait a little. Keep very still, all you three! If you move I strike, and if you do not move I strike. Oh, foolish people, who killed my Nag!"

Teddy's eyes were fixed on his father, and all his father could do was whisper, "Sit still, Teddy. You mustn't move. Teddy, keep still."

Then Rikki-tikki came up and cried, "Turn round, Nagaina. Turn and fight!"

"All in good time," said she, without moving her eyes. "I will settle my account with you presently. Look at your friends, Rikki-tikki. They are still and white. They are afraid. They dare not move, and if you come a step nearer I strike."

"Look at your eggs," said Rikki-tikki, "in the melon bed near the wall, Go and look, Nagaina!"

The big snake turned half around, and saw the egg on the veranda. "Ah-h! Give it to me," she said.

The big snake turned half around, and saw the egg on the veranda. "Ah-h! Give it to me," she said.

Rikki-tikki put his paws one on each side of the egg, and his eyes were blood-red. "What price for a snake's egg? For a young cobra? For a young king cobra? For the last—the very last of the brood? The ants are eating all the others down by the melon bed."

Nagaina spun clear round, forgetting everything for the sake of the one egg. Rikki-tikki saw Teddy's father shoot out a big hand, catch Teddy by the shoulder, and drag him across the little table with the teacups, safe and out of reach of Nagaina.

"Tricked! Tricked! Tricked! Rikk-tck-tck!" chuckled Rikki-tikki. "The boy is safe, and it was I—I—I that caught Nag by the hood last night in the bathroom." Then he began to jump up and down, all four feet

Again and again and again she struck, and each time her head came with a whack on the matting of the veranda and she gathered herself together like a watch spring.

together, his head close to the floor. "He threw me to and fro, but he could not shake me off. He was dead before the big man blew him in two. I did it! Rikki-tikki-tck-tck! Come then, Nagaina. Come and fight with me. You shall not be a widow long."

Nagaina saw that she had lost her chance of killing Teddy, and the egg lay between Rikki-tikki's paws. "Give me the egg, Rikki-tikki. Give me the last of my eggs, and I will go away and never come back," she said, lowering her hood.

"Yes, you will go away, and you will never come back. For you will go the rubbish heap with Nag. Fight, widow! The big man has gone for his gun! Fight!"

Rikki-tikki was bounding all round Nagaina, keeping just out of reach of her strike, his little eyes like hot coals. Nagaina gathered herself together and flung out at him. Rikki-tikki jumped up and backward. Again and again and again she struck, and each time her head came with a whack on the matting of the veranda and she gathered herself together like a watch spring. Then Rikki-tikki danced in a circle to get behind her, and Nagaina spun round to keep her head to his head, so that the rustle of her tail on the matting sounded like dry leaves blown along by the wind.

He had forgotten the egg. It still lay on the veranda, and Nagaina came nearer to it, till at last, while Rikki-tikki was drawing breath, she caught it in her mouth, turned to the veranda steps, and flew like an arrow down the path, with Rikki-tikki behind her. When the cobra runs for her life, she goes like a whiplash flicked across a horse's neck. Rikki-tikki knew that he must catch her, or all the trouble would begin again.

She headed straight for the long grass by the thornbush, and as he was running Rikki-tikki heard Darzee still singing his foolish little song of triumph.

But Darzee's wife was wiser. She flew off her nest as Nagaina came along, and flapped her wings about Nagaina's head. If Darzee had helped they might have turned her, but Nagaina only lowered her hood and went on. Still, the instant's delay brought Rikki-tikki up to her, and as she plunged into the rathole where she and Nag used to live, his little white teeth were clenched on her tail, and he went down with her—and very few mongooses, however wise and old they may be, care to follow a cobra into its hole.

It was dark in the hole; and Rikki-tikki never knew when it might open out and give Nagaina room to turn and strike at him. He held on savagely, and stuck out his feet to act as brakes on the dark slope of the hot, moist earth.

Then the grass by the mouth of the hole stopped waving, and Darzee said, "It is all over with Rikki-tikki! We must sing his death song. Valiant Rikki-tikki is dead! For Nagaina will surely kill him underground."

So he sang a very mournful song that he made up on the spur of the minute, and just as he got to the most touching part, the grass quivered again, and Rikki-tikki, covered with dirt, dragged himself out of the hole leg by leg, licking his whiskers. Darzee stopped with a little shout. Rikki-tikki shook some of the dust out of his fur and sneezed. "It is all over," he said. "The widow will never come out again." And the red ants that live between the grass stems heard him, and began to troop down one after another to see if he had spoken the truth.

Rikki-tikki curled himself up in the grass and slept where he was—slept and slept till it was late in the afternoon, for he had done a hard day's work.

"Now," he said, when he awoke, "I will go back to the house. Tell the Coppersmith, Darzee, and he will

It was dark in the hole; and Rikki-tikki never knew when it might open out and give Nagaina room to turn and strike at him.

Animal Antics

tell the garden that Nagaina is dead."

The Coppersmith is a bird who makes a noise exactly like the beating of a little hammer on a copper pot. The reason he is always making it is because he is the town crier to every Indian garden, and tells all the news to everybody who cares to listen. As Rikki-tikki went up the path, he heard his "attention" notes like a tiny dinner gong, and then the steady "Ding-dong-tock! Nag is dead—dong! Nagaina is dead! Ding-dong-tock!" That set all the birds in the garden singing, and the frogs croaking, for Nag and Nagaina used to eat frogs as well as little birds.

When Rikki got to the house, Teddy and Teddy's mother (she looked very white still, for she had been fainting) and Teddy's father came out and almost cried over him; and that night he ate all that was given him till he could eat no more, and went to bed on Teddy's shoulder, where Teddy's mother saw him when she came to look late at night.

"He just saved our lives and Teddy's life," she said to her husband. "Just think, he saved all our lives."

Rikki-tikki woke up with a jump, for the mongooses are light sleepers.

"Oh, it's you," said he. "What are you bothering for? All the cobras are dead. And if they weren't, I'm here."

Rikki-tikki had a right to be proud of himself. But he did not grow too proud, and he kept that garden as a mongoose should keep it, with tooth and jump and spring and bite, till never a cobra dared show its head inside the walls.

Rikki-tikki had a right to be proud of himself.

The Bremen Town Musicians

by the Brothers Grimm

At last, however, its strength was worn out and it was no longer of any use for work.

A certain man had a mule which for many years carried sacks to the mill without tiring. At last, however, its strength was worn out and it was no longer of any use for work. Accordingly, its master began to ponder as to how best to cut down its keep. But the mule, seeing there was mischief in the air, ran away and started on the road to Bremen. There he thought he could become a town musician.

When he had been traveling a short time, he fell in with a hound, who was lying panting on the road as though he had run himself off his legs.

"Well, what are you panting so for, Growler?" said the mule.

"Ah," said the hound, "just because I am old, and every day I get weaker. And also, because I can no longer keep up with the pack, my master wanted to kill me, so I took my departure. But now how am I to earn my bread?"

"Do you know what?" said the mule. "I am going to Bremen and shall there become a town musician. Come with me and take your part in the music. I shall play the lute, and you shall beat the kettledrum."

The hound agreed and they went on.

A short time afterwards they came upon a cat sitting in the road, with a face as long as a wet week.

"Well, why are you so cross, Whiskers?" asked the

mule.

"Who can be cheerful when he is out at elbows?" said the cat. "I am getting on in years and my teeth are blunted, and I prefer to sit by the stove and purr instead of hunting round after mice. Just because of this my mistress wanted to drown me. I made myself scarce, but now I don't know where to turn."

"Come with us to Bremen," said the mule. "You are a great hand at serenading, so you can become a town musician."

The cat consented and joined them.

Next the fugitives passed by a yard where a barnyard fowl was sitting on the door, crowing with all its might.

"You crow so loud you pierce one through and through," said the mule. "What is the matter?"

"Why, didn't I prophesy fine weather for Lady Day, when Our Lady washes the Christ Child's little garment and wants to dry it? But notwithstanding this, because Sunday visitors are coming tomorrow, the mistress has no pity, and she has ordered the cook to make me into soup. So I shall have my neck wrung tonight. Now I am crowing with all my might while I can."

"Come along, Red-comb," said the mule. "You had much better come with us. We are going to Bremen and you will find a much better fate there. You have a good voice, and when we make music together there will be quality in it."

The rooster allowed himself to be persuaded and they all four went off together. They could not, however, reach the town in one day, and by evening they arrived at a wood, where they determined to spend the night. The mule and the hound lay down under a big tree. The cat and the rooster settled themselves in the branches, the rooster flying right up to the top, which was the safest place for him. Before going to sleep he looked

"Come along, Red-comb," said the mule. "You had much better come with us. We are going to Bremen and you will find a much better fate there. You have a good voice, and when we make music together there will be quality in it."

Animal Antics

The mule was to take up his position with his forefeet on the window sill, the hound was to jump on his back, the cat to climb upon onto the hound, and last of all the rooster was to up and perch on the cat's head.

round once more in every direction. Suddenly it seemed that he saw a light burning in the distance. He called out to his comrades that there must be a house not far off, for he saw a light.

"Very well," said the mule. "Let us set out and make our way to it, for the entertainment here is very bad."

The hound thought some bones or meat would suit him too, so they set out in the direction of the light. They soon saw it shining more clearly and getting bigger and bigger, till they reached a brightly lighted robbers' den. The mule, being the tallest, approached the window and looked in.

"What do you see, old mule?" asked the rooster.

"What do I see?" answered the mule. "Why, a table spread with delicious food and drink, and robbers seated at it enjoying themselves."

"That would just suit us," said the rooster.

"Yes, if we were only there," answered the mule.

Then the animals took counsel as to how to set about driving the robbers out. At last they hit upon a plan.

The mule was to take up his position with his forefeet on the window sill, the hound was to jump on his back, the cat to climb upon onto the hound, and last of all the rooster was to up and perch on the cat's head. When they were thus arranged, at a given signal they all began to perform their music. The mule brayed, the hound barked, the cat mewed, and the rooster crowed. Then they dashed through the window, shivering the panes. The robbers jumped up at the terrible noise. They thought nothing less than that the devil was coming in upon them and fled into the wood in the greatest alarm. Then the four animals sat down to table and helped themselves according to taste, and they ate as though they had been starving for weeks. When they had finished, they extinguished the light and looked for sleeping places, each one to suit his taste.

The mule lay down on a pile of straw, the hound behind the door, the cat on the hearth near the warm ashes, and the rooster flew up to the rafters. As they were tired from the long journey, they soon went to sleep.

When midnight was past, and the robbers saw from a distance that the light was no longer burning and that all seemed quiet, the chief said, "We ought not to have been scared by a false alarm." And he ordered one of the robbers to go and examine the house.

Finding all quiet, the messenger went into the kitchen to kindle a light. And taking the cat's glowing, fiery eyes for live coals, he held a match close to them so as to light it. But the cat would stand no nonsense—it flew at his face, spat, and scratched. He was terribly frightened and ran away.

He tried to get out the back door, but the hound, who was lying there, jumped up and bit his leg. As he ran across the pile of straw in front of the house, the mule gave him a good sound kick with his hind legs; while the rooster, who had awakened at the uproar quite fresh and gay, cried out from his perch, "Cock-a-doodle-doo."

There upon the robber ran back as fast as he could to his chief and said, "There is a gruesome witch in the house who breathed on me and scratched me with her long fingers."

Thereupon the robber ran back as fast as he could to his chief and said, "There is a gruesome witch in the house who breathed on me and scratched me with her long fingers. Behind the door there stands a man with a knife, who stabbed me, while in the yard lies a black monster who hit me with a club. And upon the roof the judge is seated, and he called out, 'Bring the rogue here!' So I hurried away as fast as I could."

Thenceforward the robbers did not venture again to the house, which pleased the four Bremen musicians so much that they never wished to leave it again.

Animal Antics

Hearthside
Lullabies

In this essay, I tried to prove that Charles Dickens' greatest artistic Old Friend was the childhood glee he retained his entire life.

The inconvenience, complexities, and complications of daily air travel make my career a decidedly mixed blessing.

Hearthside Lullabies

Essay

by Dr. Engel

Since I have been on leave from the English Department at my university, I have lectured in forty-five states on many writers but especially on Charles Dickens, my favorite author. I have been delighted to address these groups and have enjoyed visiting so many new cities. But the inconvenience, complexities, and complications of daily air travel make my career a decidedly mixed blessing. To put it theologically, the audiences are heavenly; the traveling is hell.

Though my complaints about air travel are numerous, they do not often include tedium. As all frequent fliers know, the view outside of an airplane window is on occasion so spectacular in its beauty and serenity that it helps to compensate for the dullness inherent in constant flying.

I vividly remember one early morning flight that I took from New Orleans to Tampa. As we ascended from the New Orleans airport, we followed the course of the Mississippi River to its mouth, where it emptied into the Gulf of Mexico. I shall never forget that view from 10,000 feet. The sun had just risen, and since we were headed East, it cast a purple-golden hue onto the rushing waters of the river far below as they spilled into the seemingly endless Gulf of Mexico. And framing the view in the distance were the puffiest, purest clouds I had ever seen, suffused with yellow and pink from the rising sun, looking like so many tufts of pastel cotton candy.

As I gaped at this rare display of nature's grandeur I

happened to look around at my fellow passengers. I was on a small commuter plane with only about twenty others. Not one of them had even glanced out to see the spectacular convergence of river, gulf, and rising sun. Some had their noses buried in USA Today; others were asleep with jaws dropped, not in wonder as mine had been but in the oblivion of deep slumber.

It was possible that some of them were regulars who took this same flight so often that the loveliness had diminished through familiarity. But I could not help thinking as I gazed at the overwhelming beauty of the scene outside my window what the pen of Charles Dickens could have produced had he been alive to glimpse such a vista. His sense of awe at natural beauty combined with his genius for description could have created a paean of infinite inspiration. Of course, none of us on that plane possessed the brilliance of Dickens' combination of wonder and joy.

But I was wrong. For suddenly across the aisle and two rows up, I saw in one passenger's expression the enchantment and delight of a Dickens. The passenger was not even looking out the window, but the wonder was more than evident in his face. In fact, my fellow traveler was a one-year-old child, the type I usually avoid because of the rambunctious turbulence which usually accompanies him. The passenger behind him was a grandmotherly, jolly soul who was engaging him in an intense game of peek-a-boo which enthralled the child. Each time the woman popped her head up from behind the child's seat cushion, he reacted with a chortle of astonishment and joy. His eyes were as wide and appreciative as mine had been staring at the clouds and river.

That toddler made me remember my own early childhood when my father would lock his thumbs

His sense of awe at natural beauty combined with his genius for description could have created a paean of infinite inspiration.

I saw the same fresh delight with which Charles Dickens viewed and recorded the world and which made him a uniquely sensitive and brilliant writer.

together and flap his arching fingers in perfect imitation of wings. He accompanied this with a haunting whistle, that only he could make, sounding just like a songbird in flight. I was utterly enchanted by this charade over and over again as was his grandson, my nephew, some thirty years later.

And in that child's face on the plane, I saw the same fresh delight with which Charles Dickens viewed and recorded the world and which made him a uniquely sensitive and brilliant writer. Perhaps his greatest artistic gift was to retain somehow a child's reverence and glee for the most everyday experiences that the rest of us lose as we age and settle into our tedious adult routines. How fortunate that in the earliest months of life we do not need a fantastic panorama to dazzle us at 10,000 feet. Our own two feet will do just as nicely when we watch our toes wiggle, and we squeal with delight in our little beds. Too many critics have ascribed Charles Dickens' unique vision as being filtered through the bars of that debtor's prison he experienced in adolescence. On the contrary, I believe his most inspired writing was the result of the vision we all experience through the bars of our own cribs in infancy. But only Dickens could retain the childlike magic of that fresh view during his entire life and thereby turn his fictional world into a perpetual playground of mythic delights.

Alfred Tennyson

Alfred Tennyson was born in 1809 at exactly the stroke of midnight between August 5th and 6th—so there has always been a question about his actual birthday. He was one of 10 children and always had lots of pets, including a monkey. One Sunday morning when he was 7, Tennyson was unable to attend church because of a sore throat. His brother gave him a slate to write on to pass the time. Tennyson wrote his first poem about a flower and the poem is still published and read today. He always thought the best way to write poetry was to come up with one good line and then write the rest of the poem around it. He was named Poet Laureate of England at the early age of 41 and held the honor for 41 more years until his death.

This Singing World

by Alfred Tennyson

Sweet and low, breathe and blow,
Wind of the western sea!
Over the rolling waters go,
Come from the dying moon, and blow,
Blow him again to me;
While my little one, while my pretty one sleeps.

Sleep and rest, sleep and rest,
Father will come to thee soon;
Rest, rest, on mother's breast,
Father will come to thee soon;
Father will come to his babe in the nest,
Silver sails all out of the west
Under the silver moon;
Sleep, my little one, sleep, my pretty one, sleep.

Sleep, My Child

An Old Welsh Lullaby

Sleep, my child,
And peace attend thee,
All through the night.
Guardian angels
I will send thee
All through the night.
Soft the drowsy hours are creeping,
Hill and vale in slumber steeping,
I my loving vigil keeping
All through the night.

Welsh Folktales

When Llywelyn the Last—the first, and as yet, the only—WELSH Prince of Wales was accidentally killed 700 years ago, the political independence of Wales died with him. Through the centuries of oppression, the Welsh imagination has remained strong, buried deep in the Celtic traditions of the past. These ancient tales and traditions are best remembered today by the people who still speak the Welsh language (and the figure is increasing every year).

Bed in Summer

by Robert Louis Stevenson

And I should like so much to play
To have to go to bed by day?

In winter I get up at night
And dress by yellow candle-light.
In summer, quite the other way,
I have to go to bed by day.

I have to go to bed and see
The birds still hopping on the tree,
Or hear the grown-up people's feet
Still going past me in the street.

And does it not seem hard to you
When all the sky is clear and blue,
And I should like so much to play
To have to go to bed by day?

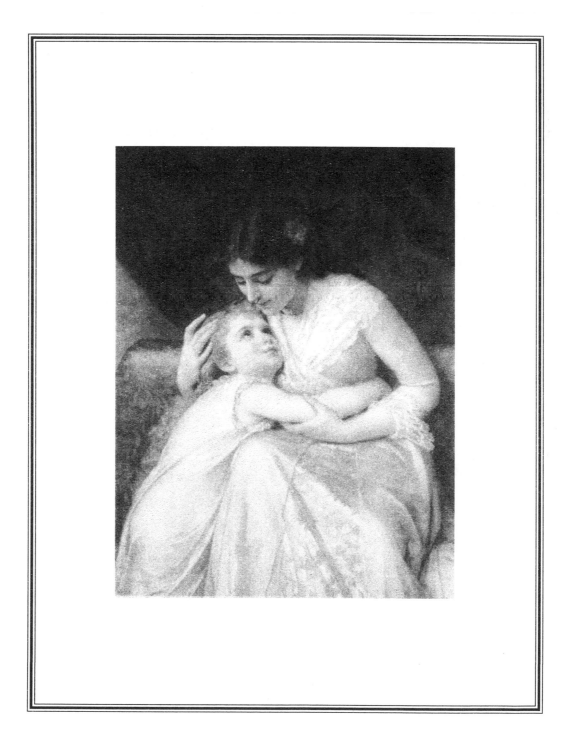

Eugene Field

*Eugene Field was one of the few poets who wrote only children's poetry, thus the nickname, **The Children's Poet**. He was born in St. Louis, Missouri, in 1850, but his mother died when he was six. He wrote his first poem (about his dog, Fido) when he was nine. His father died when he was 19 and he spent his inheritance traveling around Europe. He became well known for a witty column he wrote for a Chicago newspaper. He had eight children of his own, but died early at 45. Today, the Field House and Toy Museum are open to the public in St. Louis.*

Wynken, Blynken, and Nod

by Eugene Field

Wynken, Blynken, and Nod one night
Sailed off in a wooden shoe—
Sailed on a river of crystal light,
Into a sea of dew.
"Where are you going, and what do you wish?"
The old moon asked the three.
"We have come to fish for the herring-fish
That live in this beautiful sea;
Nets of silver and gold have we!"
Said Wynken, Blynken, and Nod.

The old moon laughed and sang a song,
As they rocked in the wooden shoe,
And the wind that sped them all night long
Ruffled the waves of dew.
The little stars were the herring-fish
That lived in that beautiful sea—
"Now cast your nets wherever you wish—
But never afeared are we!"
So cried the stars to the fishermen three;
Wynken, Blynken, and Nod.

All night long their nets they threw
To the stars in the twinkling foam—
Then down from the skies came the wooden shoe,

Bringing the fishermen home;
'Twas all so pretty a sail, it seemed
As if it could not be,
And some folks thought 'twas a dream they dreamed
Of sailing that beautiful sea—
But I shall name you the fisherman three;
Wynken, Blynken, and Nod.

Wynken and Blynken are two little eyes,
And Nod is a little head,
And the wooden shoe that sailed the skies
Is a wee one's trundle-bed.
So shut your eyes while mother sings
Of wonderful sights that be,
And you shall see the beautiful things
As you rock on the misty sea,
Where the old shoe rocked the fisherman three;
Wynken, Blynken, and Nod.

*And the wooden shoe that
sailed the skies
Is a wee one's trundle-bed.*

Hans Christian Andersen

Hans Christian Andersen was a Danish author famous for his many fairy tales. Born in 1805, he received very little education, was very poor, and experienced many emotional upsets because of his height and epileptic seizures. He ran away to Copenhagen, Denmark, at age 14, and began a career as a singer, dancer, and actor. His first book of fairy tales was published at Christmas and he became instantly famous. For 37 years, he published volumes of his fairy tales (more than 150 stories) that established him as one of the great figures of world literature. He never married, and died at the age of 75 at his home. Today, the **Hans Christian Andersen Award** *is given to authors or illustrators who make a lasting contribution to children's literature.*

Ole Shut-Eyes, the Sandman

Adapted from Hans Christian Andersen

There is nobody in all the world who can tell so many stories as Old Shut-Eyes, the Sandman. Evenings when the children are sitting around the table or on their little footstools just as good as possible, Ole, the Sandman, comes and suddenly the children all feel very sleepy and want to go to bed. And when they are tucked in snug and have gone quite fast asleep, Ole sits on their beds. He is gaily dressed in silk that shines red, green, and blue with every turn he makes, and he holds up over their heads a wonderful-colored umbrella with many pictures on it. Then under his great umbrella the children dream beautiful dreams.

Technical Details

Illustrations

Quinn Hawkesworth
Carl Gilfillan
*Zedcor, Inc. **Desk Gallery***
*IMSI **Masterclips***
*Corel **Gallery***
*Broderbund **ClickArt***
*Nova Development Corporation **Art Explosion***
Dover Publications
Library of Congress

Paper

Printed on Accent Opaque 60#

Dr. Engel's programs about literary authors and their writings always feature interesting facts and trivia that make learning fun for students. In addition to the authors featured in this book, he has audio programs about these authors:

Charles Dickens

Charlotte and Emily Brontë

Margaret Mitchell

George Eliot

Jane Austen

Robert & Elizabeth Barrett Browning

Wordsworth and Byron

Oscar Wilde

Thomas Hardy

Anthony Trollope

William Makepeace Thackeray

Ernest Hemingway

Sir Arthur Conan Doyle

Sir Walter Scott

Winston Churchill

Christopher Columbus

Robert E. Lee

Sir Walter Raleigh

Geoffrey Chaucer

F. Scott Fitzgerald

E. B. White

D. H. Lawrence

T. S. Eliot

L. Frank Baum

James Joyce and W.B. Yeats

Anton Chekhov

To order a current catalog write to:

Authors Ink
203 Killingsworth Drive
Cary, NC 27511

*You may also call toll free to **(800) 392-4434***

Catalogs and Dr. Engel's programs may also be ordered on the internet at:

www.AuthorsInk.com